Class **9c** and the
Genesis
Time Machine

Text copyright © Mike Coles 2006
The author asserts the moral right
to be identified as the author of this work

Published by
The Bible Reading Fellowship
First Floor, Elsfield Hall
15–17 Elsfield Way, Oxford OX2 8FG
Website: www.brf.org.uk

ISBN-10: 1 84101 440 0
ISBN-13: 978 1 84101 440 1

First published 2006
10 9 8 7 6 5 4 3 2 1 0

Acknowledgments
Unless otherwise stated, scripture quotations are taken from the
Good News Bible published by The Bible Societies/HarperCollins
Publishers Ltd, UK © American Bible Society 1966, 1971, 1976,
1992, used with permission.

A catalogue record for this book is available from the British Library

Printed in Singapore by Craft Print International Ltd

Class 9c and the
Genesis
Time Machine

Mike Coles

Contents

Introduction

This is the remarkable story of one teacher, ten pupils, and a time machine! Mike Coles is the Head of Religious Education at a Church of England secondary school in the heart of London's East End.

It's a perfect example of a multi-cultural school. Being a Church of England school, it is there to serve the community. There is a large Muslim population living in Stepney, mainly from Bangladesh, and many of the families send their children to the school.

The school also has many Christian children, whose families are from all over the world. They come from places such as the West Indies, Africa, Ireland, the UK, Russia and the Ukraine, and they have a variety of church backgrounds including Anglican, Roman Catholic, Baptist, Methodist, Pentecostal and Orthodox. Once again, it's a great mix! Mike finds that being Head of RE in a school like this is an amazing experience. There's no better place to teach.

An important part of his job is organizing school trips for his pupils, to local churches, mosques, Buddhist centres and so on. Now he's about to organize the most amazing trip that any pupil from any school in the world will ever have experienced.

Mike has selected ten pupils from his form, 9C, to attend an RE trip. They have been studying the Bible and the book of Genesis, and he has told the class that he's organizing a special outing to help with their studies. Everybody in the class wanted to come along, but the school minibus can only seat ten pupils, so Mike put all their names in a hat (one of the boys' baseball caps, actually) and drew out five boys' names and five girls' names.

Here are the ten pupils chosen to go on this remarkable school trip. You'll get to learn a great deal more about them as the story enfolds.

The five girls

Bronagh: A Roman Catholic from Ireland, Bronagh is very able academically, but at the same time very down to earth. She has a great sense of humour and she loves listening to rock music.

Shaheda: Shaheda is a Muslim girl whose family is originally from Bangladesh. She is a hardworking girl, and quite shy.

Natasha: Natasha's family is originally from Barbados in the West Indies. She is a Pentecostal Christian, and is diligent, enthusiastic and high-spirited with a great sense of humour and a love of singing.

Sarah: Sarah is from Bethnal Green. She has no real faith, but really enjoys RE lessons. She also has a good sense of humour, although she can be a little cheeky from time to time.

Doyin: Doyin's family is originally from Nigeria. She is always talking and asking questions, particularly about current affairs, which she loves discussing. She is full of life and there is never a dull moment with her around.

The five boys

Jilani: Jilani is a Muslim, born in Bangladesh. He is sometimes the class clown, but although he's noisy, he does work hard and is a really likeable character.

Steven: Steven is of Jamaican origin. He attends a Baptist church with his family. He is very intelligent, but can be lazy—one of those who will do well in his exams with little effort!

Boris: Boris is an Orthodox Christian from the Ukraine. He is quiet, studious and fairly shy.

John: John lives in Stratford, in north-east London, where he goes to an Anglican church. He loves to debate and is always asking questions.

Alan: Born and brought up in Whitechapel, Alan has no faith background. He's a real East End lad, cheeky and a bit of a crafty rogue. He can work well, when he wants to do so!

So these are the ten pupils who have been chosen, but what exactly is this amazing school trip? When Mike wrote a letter to the pupils' parents about it, he told them that it was a trip to help them gain a deeper knowledge and understanding of some of the stories in the book of Genesis. The letter described the journey as a 'mystery tour' and assured parents that the pupils would all thoroughly enjoy the experience.

The parents are happy to sign the letter and give permission, as it is a school trip and will be properly supervised. As it's an RE trip, they are confident that it will be particularly good for the kids! What the parents do not know, however, is that Mike will be taking the ten pupils back in a time machine.

When the pupils get into the school minibus, Mike will explain it all to them, as simply as he can. Yes, hard as it is to believe, they will be travelling back in time. He'll try to tell them a little about how it is possible, about quantum physics and Einstein's theory of relativity. (Good luck to him!)

The pupils will obviously not believe a word of it and will just think that Mike is acting daft, as is often the case. He will reply that he totally understands, but they must believe him. It is an RE trip, so they must have faith! He will give the pupils one last chance to decide whether they would rather stay at school. He'll tell them that it will be an awesome experience and even quite terrifying at first, but they are to trust him.

Before joining Mike and the ten pupils on the time-travelling school minibus, it's worth knowing what they will all be witnessing first-hand. Mike will programme the time machine to return to the very moment of creation, the beginning of the book of Genesis. They will witness the very beginning of the earth. Will it be exactly as recorded in the Bible, or is the reality quite different? Were there dinosaurs? Did Adam and Eve exist? If they did, did they go around naked, and if so, how will the pupils react when they see this? So many questions... and all about to be answered!

The school party will see what happened between Cain and Abel. They'll experience the terrifying flood and watch Noah build his ark. Mike will try his best to give a commentary on what is happening around the minibus, while also trying to answer the pupils' questions and keep control. The story starts with Mike getting the pupils into the bus, explaining exactly where they are going and how, and giving them strict guidelines about how to behave when time travelling. So buckle up and prepare to experience what really happened 'in the beginning'.

Chapter 1

Back in time

'OK folks!' shouts Mr Coles. 'Let's all get on the bus now. Alan, could you quickly collect the packed lunches from the staff room, please?'

'Why's it always me?' moans Alan. He runs off towards the staff room, mumbling to himself. He's there and back within two minutes. Mr Coles helps Alan load the box of food into the back of the minibus.

'Where is it we're going, sir?' asks Sarah. 'Not to some boring old church to listen to some boring old priest?'

'When you're all sat down, I'll explain everything to you.' Mr Coles surveys them sternly. They immediately go quiet and wait eagerly to hear what this mystery tour is all about—the tour that is supposed to help them understand 'a little better' the first few chapters of the book of Genesis.

Mr Coles continues. 'What I'm about to tell you is going to sound unbelievable. You'll think I'm just messing around.'

'You usually mess around and play silly jokes!' shouts out Doyin.

'Yes, thank you, Doyin. You're quite right, and that is going to make it even more difficult for you all to believe what I'm about to tell you.'

All ten kids on board seem intrigued. They have never been on a mystery tour before, and they are beginning to guess that Mr Coles really does have something quite amazing to tell them.

Mr Coles picks up his copy of the Bible and turns to the book of Genesis. 'We have been looking at the creation story in this book,' he says to them. 'I know that some of you, like Sarah and Alan, think it's just a daft old story. Steven and Natasha believe the story word for word as they've been taught in their churches. And, as

Muslims, Jilani and Shaheda believe in a fairly similar creation account. The rest of you believe that God did create the world, but not in the way it's portrayed in Genesis. We've had some really good discussions in class about this book of the Bible.

'The amazing thing that I now have to tell you is this. Today we are going to find out how the world was created. We're going to discover what it was like at the very beginning. We will witness everything—the whole of creation, Adam and Eve…'

'Hold on a minute, sir,' interrupts Jilani. 'The only way we could know any of these things is if we were actually there. So what are you talking about?'

'We are going to be there. We're going back in time. We're going back to the moment of creation,' says Mr Coles, so excited he can hardly get the words out.

'I think he's really lost it this time!' Alan tells the others. 'How can this clapped-out school minibus even get us to Bethnal Green, let alone chapter one of bloomin' Genesis?'

Mr Coles and all the others find Alan's comment funny, and they exchange grins.

'Let me try to answer that if I can,' says Mr Coles, waving with his hand to get their attention. 'I don't really want to spend any time explaining how we're going to manage this trip. You have to trust me totally. You've been on many trips with me before and you've always enjoyed them. Today's trip will be the most amazing one that any school pupil from any school on this planet has ever been on. You can't get more exciting than that.'

Mr Coles then opens up a small cabinet on the dashboard of the minibus. The pupils suddenly find themselves looking at the most bizarre metallic object they have ever seen.

'That looks like something out of *Star Trek*,' John blurts out.

'In a way, it is,' Mr Coles replies. 'All I can tell you is that this strange object was given to me by someone, and it doesn't matter who. I was told it comes from the future, and quite simply it enables us to travel back in time. There's no point you all asking me how it works, because I haven't a clue.'

'How does it work?' asks Jilani.

'Very funny,' says Bronagh and pulls a silly face at Jilani.

'This trip will be both terrifying and spectacular at the same time,' Mr Coles goes on. 'I'm not forcing anyone to go. If you feel that it will be a little bit too much of a mystery tour, you may leave now. Also, if any of you start finding it all too much when we get started, we can always return to this point in time immediately.'

'I suppose we could return to yesterday if we wanted,' says Boris thoughtfully. 'Or we could go back to last year!'

'Time travel is a confusing concept for any of us even to begin to understand.' Mr Coles turns to him. 'But no matter. We have a device here that will enable us to go back to the creation of the earth.'

'I'm not sure if you're winding us up or not,' says John, 'but it sounds like it's going to be a fun trip, no matter what.'

'I think John's right,' adds Natasha. 'Let's get going.'

'Well,' sighs Mr Coles, 'I suppose the only way any of you are going to believe me is if we just get this show on the road. I should point out one thing, though. When we do travel back in time, this strange device on the dashboard will emit a beam all around the minibus. When we get to the places we'll be visiting, we must always stay within the beam. By doing this, we will prevent any quantum paradoxes from occurring.'

'What's one of those when it's at home?' asks Doyin.

Mr Coles looks at Doyin. 'To put it simply, we must not interfere with anything from the past. We must not breathe the air, pick up a blade of grass or step on an ant. If we were to do this, we might change everything. Imagine if you went back in time and somehow ended up killing your great-grandmother! You would cease to exist and you would change the whole course of history. And even making a tiny change—like stepping on an ant—could have a huge effect. But don't worry, the beam will keep us safe.' He smiles round at the group.

'Well, we could stand here all day discussing time travel and we'd be just as confused. I'd like you all to buckle up—that's if you're sure you still want to go on the trip. Would anyone like to leave now?'

They all look around at each other. Will anyone leave? No one seems to want to lose face in front of their mates. No hands go up. They sit there in silence. Things have suddenly got a little tense on board the bus. Then Alan suddenly lets rip a loud burp. For a few moments their thoughts are taken away from the mystery that lies ahead and they giggle wildly, as kids do whenever someone burps in front of the teacher.

'Sorry, sir,' says Alan. 'It must be nerves!'

'Settle down now, folks,' says Mr Coles. 'We're going to set off. I'll be driving for about half an hour, first heading towards Essex on the A12. We need to find a quiet stretch of road before we can activate the time machine.'

'I still think we're off to some boring old church,' moans Sarah.

'We'll see,' Bronagh says to her, with a wink. 'I think we need to keep a close eye on Mr Coles!'

After a slow trek through the east London traffic and up the A12, they reach a quiet little country road just outside Brentwood. Mr Coles stops the minibus and says, 'Now's the time. This device allows me to type in a sentence about a moment in history, and we will be transported straight there. I've typed in "The Creation of the World (Genesis)". This is your last chance to say if you'd like to go back to school. It will be scary at first, but trust me: no one will be in any danger. You will find out once and for all exactly what it was like "in the beginning". OK, sit back and enjoy the ride. We're going back in time!'

Chapter 2

In the beginning

When Mr Coles looks round again, he sees that Bronagh is listening to her iPod.

'Bronagh!' he shouts, making sure that she hears him. 'We're about to travel back in time—something no one has ever done—and you're sat there listening to your music!'

'Ah, but it is Phil Collins and Genesis,' she smiles. 'I thought it might be appropriate!'

'Nice one!' shouts Jilani.

'If it helps you relax, then keep listening,' Mr Coles laughs. 'But I bet you'll soon remove those headphones as we start our journey in time! Well, here we go, everyone. Remember, don't panic.'

They all watch as he presses the central panel in the strange metallic object.

'Nothing's happening,' whispers John loudly.

'Hold on a sec!' Alan points at a tree in front of them. 'Look at that tree! It's stretching!'

Bronagh immediately takes off her headphones as predicted. She looks totally shocked as she stares out of the window. Before their very eyes, everything is stretching. The whole world seems to be distorting.

'What's happening?' screams Sarah. 'You weren't joking, were you, sir? Are we really going back in time?'

All ten pupils are open-mouthed at what is happening.

'Yes, folks, we are going back in time. I wasn't joking,' Mr Coles replies. 'If anyone wants me to stop, just let me know. But there is nothing to worry about.'

'What's actually going on out there?' asks John.

'It's going to take a few more minutes of bending and distorting before we get to where we're heading,' Mr Coles answers. 'So I'll try to explain. Now remember, I am no expert in time travel. Has anyone heard of Albert Einstein?'

'Mr Coles,' laughs Sarah, 'we might be stupid, but not that stupid. Of course we've heard of Einstein.'

'Yes,' says Boris. 'I've heard of his theory of relativity.'

'That's exactly it!' says Mr Coles. 'Einstein basically taught that we should not think of space and time as two totally different things. He said that they were both interlinked in a single, pliable framework called "space-time". He said that both space and time could be distorted and…'

Suddenly the quiet little Essex road and the beautiful countryside around them become a huge blur. The bus now seems to be moving towards a dark corner of the blurred distortion surrounding them. The pupils look terrified and sit clutching at their seats for dear life.

'I'll continue the Einstein theory a little later.' Mr Coles realizes that the pupils are so overawed by what's happening outside, they can't hear him. 'The black area we are heading for is our route through this space-time distortion. It will take us to the beginning of the creation of our planet. Here we go.'

Within a few seconds, the bus is surrounded by the deepest darkness imaginable. Everyone is silent. The darkness outside is silent. But suddenly, the bus is engulfed in a ferocious storm, and they seem to be in the middle of a raging ocean. Some of the kids on board start screaming.

'Where the hell are we?' yells Alan. 'This isn't the beginning of time! You've driven us into a bloomin' river and we're all going to drown!'

'Quiet, everyone!' shouts Mr Coles. 'Listen to me, all of you. This time machine device is very powerful and will always protect us wherever we are. I told you earlier that parts of this trip would be very scary.'

'You're not wrong!' gasps Shaheda. 'Where are we? I'm really frightened. I can't swim. I hate storms.'

While the bus fills with panic, the wind outside continues howling, and the children feel that they are floating up and down on the invisible waves. The darkness remains unbroken. After a few moments, though, despite the chaos outside, they slowly begin to settle down, realizing that the bus itself is perfectly solid and safe.

'Mr Coles,' says Doyin. 'Is this really the beginning of time?'

'I know you're all scared, but listen. The answer to Doyin's question is outside the bus right now. This is the beginning. Open your Bibles, please.' Mr Coles speaks firmly, calling the class to order. Some of them are still stunned at what is happening, and they take a while to dig out their Bibles. Eventually, all ten pupils, sitting in a minibus at the beginning of creation, manage to turn to Genesis chapter 1.

'Boris, could you please read verses 1 and 2 out loud,' asks Mr Coles, 'and the rest of you can follow.'

Boris starts to read clearly, his deep voice (exceptional for a 14-year-old!) carrying above the noise of the wind and waves outside:

In the beginning, when God created the universe, the earth was formless and desolate. The raging ocean that covered everything was engulfed in total darkness, and the power of God was moving over the water.[1]

'Thank you, Boris,' says Mr Coles. 'That was beautifully read!'

'My God!' shouts Bronagh. 'This really is the beginning!'

'Watch the "my God", please, Bronagh. Now is not the best time to misuse God's name.' Mr Coles looks over at her, raising an eyebrow to underline his point.

'You know, sir, Bronagh is right.' Natasha peers out of the window, even though there is nothing to see. 'We're in this bus surrounded by this terrible storm, and we seem to be in the middle of the ocean, moving up and down on the waves. It's exactly what Genesis says about the "raging ocean" stuff, and my pastor at church told me that the power of God could also mean a mighty wind. It's all happening as the Bible and my pastor said.'

'I was told the same thing at my church,' adds Steven.

'Let's wait and see what happens,' says John. 'I truly believe that God is the creator of everything. The Bible certainly teaches that, although I've never been sure if the creation account in Genesis is historically true.'

'I've never believed in any of it.' Alan looks thoughtful. 'But I have to admit that so far, even though we've only covered two verses, they seem to be happening outside!'

The ever-observant and questioning John then asks, 'Sir, if this is the beginning of everything, how come there is already a raging ocean and big storm out there? When was this ocean made?'

'Hey! That's a great question!' shouts Doyin.

'I was thinking the same thing as John,' adds Jilani.

'Yeah, yeah,' laughs Sarah. 'You just want to sound intelligent!'

'I've got more brains than you.' Jilani sticks his tongue out at Sarah.

Mr Coles calms them all down and tries to sum up what's been happening so far.

'It would seem that at the beginning of the six days of creation, the earth has not yet been formed into any shape, and what there is appears to be covered by this ocean. I think that planet earth already exists in a primitive form and is just surrounded by darkness. I believe that Natasha is right—'

'I always am,' she breaks in smugly.

'Perhaps sometimes,' Mr Coles continues. 'As I was saying, Natasha is right to say that when we read about the "power of God", it can refer to a mighty wind or storm.'

'Do you mind if I say something?' asks Shaheda.

'Don't be silly! Speak away,' Mr Coles responds with a smile.

'I just thought I'd mention, from a Muslim point of view, that the Qur'an also says that there was water or an ocean in the beginning. If you don't mind, I'll share a couple of verses.'

'We're all here to learn and understand. Please tell us more,' says Mr Coles encouragingly.

'The Qur'an clearly teaches that God created all living things out of the water.' Shaheda goes on, reciting from memory. "Do not the unbelievers see that the heavens and the earth were closed up, so we split them, and we made from water everything living?"[2] "And God has created every walking life out of water."[3] So the ocean we are seeing outside was written about in the Bible and in the Qur'an.'

'To sum up, then, folks,' says Mr Coles, 'what we can hear and feel all around us is the water, the raging water mentioned both in the Bible and the Qur'an. Thanks for sharing that with us, Shaheda.' Some of the class give her a little round of applause, as they sometimes do when one of them does something impressive.

'Could you all please look in your Bibles again,' Mr Coles continues. They all flick to the correct page. 'OK, everyone. You can all see in verse 3 what is about to happen. God is going to give his first creative command. Everyone look out of your nearest window. According to our time machine, creation should be any moment now.'

Chapter 3

Then God commanded...

They all sit in silence, waiting for that most famous of all commands: 'Let there be light!' The kids are on the edge of their seats, knowing that God's enormous creative powers are about to be unleashed. How will it happen? Are they safe? Is all this really happening? There are so many questions buzzing around in their heads!

It is Jilani who suddenly jumps up and shouts out, 'Did you hear that? God just spoke in Bengali!'

'No, it was Ukrainian!' shouts Boris.

'It was clearly Yoruba!' Doyin says emphatically.

Mr Coles speaks up. 'Everyone has just heard God speak in their own language! I heard God speak in English.'

'I can't believe it!' says Alan. 'I've just heard a voice too, and it was from none of you. I've never believed in God, but whatever I heard, it could only have been his voice!'

'What did the voice say?' asks Jilani.

'It said, "Let there be light,"' Alan responds, shaking his head in surprise.

'What we have just heard was God's first command…' No sooner has Mr Coles started to speak than they all hear the most ferocious wind imaginable. It sounds like 20 hurricanes raging at once. Despite its ferocity, the protective beam around the time machine must be keeping the class safe. They are beginning to trust this strange device from the future.

After a moment or two, Alan points excitedly out of the window, shouting 'Here! Look at this, sir!'

Mr Coles and the others look out of the windows on the side

where Alan is sitting. Very slowly, but very surely, they can see tiny rays of light beginning to flicker from way above. It is an amazing sight after such a long time surrounded by total darkness.

'I think I now understand why there is such a big wind outside,' says Mr Coles slowly. 'It's actually blowing away the darkness!'

'You're right, sir!' answers Bronagh. 'If you look outside now, the light is getting brighter and you can see dark clouds and vapours swirling around, as if they're starting to disappear.'

Steven, who always likes to look cool, reaches inside his jacket pocket and produces a pair of shades. He slips them on, along with his baseball cap.

'Just getting ready for this bright and beautiful day,' he says casually.

The others laugh.

'You know, sir,' says John, who's been sitting still, looking thoughtful, 'I don't think God actually created light at this moment.'

'What are you on about?' asks Sarah. 'What's that happening outside, then?'

'What I mean is that the light was already there.'

'I think John is right,' Mr Coles agrees. 'I think that just as the water already existed before God actually spoke, so did the sun, the moon and the stars. They may already have been in existence for millions of years before these six days of creation.'

'And their light couldn't reach through because of all the clouds and vapours,' says Jilani, looking really pleased with himself for following all that is being discussed.

'Well done, Jilani!' says Mr Coles. 'The thick clouds that are being blown away by the wind are obviously heavy water vapour and perhaps even frozen ice. There might have also been some vapours coming from the earth through the water. Don't forget that the earth might also be millions or even billions of years old.'

It all goes quiet on the minibus. Everyone sits there in amazement, staring out of the windows. After a while, the howling wind stops blowing. All that can be seen is white light, everywhere. The bus is bobbing up and down on the ocean; everything else is white. There is no sky as such, just whiteness as far as they can see.

'It's whiter than white,' chuckles Natasha, 'just like my mum's washing powder!'

They laugh at this, but Natasha is right. The whiteness is unbelievably brilliant, hurting their eyes if they stare at it for too long.

'Where is the sky?' asks Bronagh.

'At the moment, Bronagh, God has simply blown away the darkness to let the sun's light shine through,' answers Mr Coles. 'What I'm going to do now is to turn this dial on our time machine to speed things up a little. I'll make the hours pass as if they were just a few minutes. Here we go.'

Mr Coles turns the dial very slowly. After a few seconds, the bright light outside starts to fade away.

'What are you doing, sir?' asks Jilani. 'We don't want to be in the dark again!'

'Don't worry,' says Doyin. 'Now that we have light outside, we're going to start having days and nights. That's what sir is doing. He's just speeded time up a little and it's now becoming night-time.'

'That's right,' adds Boris. 'Remember that the earth still spins on its own axis, and now that we have light we'll be able to distinguish night and day.'

'Well done, folks!' shouts Mr Coles, delighted that they're working things out for themselves. That's what teaching is all about!

'And now,' says Jilani, 'thanks to this light that's coming through, we can have a night and day, just like it says in Genesis.'

'If you carry on like this, Jilani,' laughs Natasha, 'we'll soon be calling you Professor.' Jilani sits there looking smug.

Within a few minutes it is again pitch black outside. Mr Coles tells them that that was the first day, and with the time machine running at its present speed, it will be day two shortly. 'Shall we sleep for two minutes, then?' asks Doyin.

'Very funny,' says Steven. 'Is it worth taking off my shades, or shall I just leave them on, as the night will only last for a few minutes?' He turns to Mr Coles. 'Sir, a whole day has gone by and it's almost day two, so when are we going to eat our packed lunch?'

'That's a good question, Steven,' replies Mr Coles. 'But remember, we've only been on the bus for a short while. Lunch may not be until day four or five. We'll have to see.'

'I might have to tell my mum that you didn't feed us for five days!' teases Natasha.

'That will be tricky, seeing as we'll be returning on the same day that we left,' giggles Doyin.

As they are all laughing away, they notice that it's beginning to get light outside again. Then everything looks as it did a few minutes before, with a bright white light surrounding the bus.

'OK, everyone,' says Mr Coles. 'I've set the time machine to run at normal speed again. We're about to witness God's creative power on day two.'

Alan calls out, 'Sir, when can we go to the loo? I need a pee!'

'We've only just left,' John moans, 'and we're about to watch God at work, and all you can think about is going for a pee!'

'I think Alan is going to have to wait until tomorrow, day three,' adds Bronagh.

'Why?' asks Shaheda.

''Cos that's when he creates trees, and Alan will need a tree to pee behind!' Bronagh retorts.

The others laugh. Mr Coles, still laughing, says, 'Bronagh is correct. You'll need to wait until tomorrow before you can go to the loo, and before you start complaining, remember we have the time machine. Tomorrow need only be a few minutes away if we wish, so just wait a bit.'

'Yeah! Just cross your legs,' laughs Jilani.

'OK, class,' says Mr Coles. 'Could you all turn to Genesis chapter 1, verses 6 to 8. Doyin, could you read, please?'

'OK, sir.'

Then God commanded, 'Let there be a dome to divide the water and to keep it in two separate places'—and it was done. So God made a dome,

and it separated the water under it from the water above it. He named the
dome 'Sky'. Evening passed and morning came—that was the second day.

'Thanks, Doyin,' says Mr Coles. 'Let's wait and see what happens during day two.'

'Let's hope it's quick,' Alan grumbles, looking a little uncomfortable. 'I'm bursting for the loo.'

Just as on day one, the whole class suddenly goes silent. Once again, in their own languages, they hear the voice of God. And what God says is exactly what's written in Genesis.

'God is going to create the sky!' calls out Boris.

'I heard it too!' exclaims Jilani, looking really excited.

'Let's see what happens,' says Mr Coles.

'This will be interesting,' adds John. 'I've never really understood this idea about the dome.'

No sooner has John said this than there is the most deafening noise outside. As they look through the windows, all they can see is steam and fire coming out of the water surrounding them. There seems to be huge seismic activity going on beneath the surface. 'Remember, folks,' calls out Mr Coles, 'we are perfectly safe in here, no matter what goes on out there.'

Mr Coles is right. In theory the bus should have disintegrated within seconds as a result of what is happening outside, but they are fine. The ocean seems to be boiling, and steam and vapour continue to shoot up into the white light all around.

'This looks like it may continue for a while, so I'll speed things up a little to take us closer to the end of the day,' says Mr Coles. He fiddles with the correct dial, and before they know it, everything starts to calm down.

Sarah suddenly shouts, 'Look, sir! There are clouds above us. Before, it was totally white, but now it's a bit grey and there are clouds everywhere.'

'Just like a typical English day,' laughs Bronagh.

'So that's what all the boiling of the water was about,' says Mr Coles. 'It produced vapour to form clouds, and now that there are clouds above us, I suppose it's the first time we can say that there is a "sky". That's day two, folks. God has created the sky.'

'But where's the sun?' asks Steven.

'The light of the sun is getting through,' Mr Coles replies. 'That's what the whiteness is all about, but there is still so much water vapour in the air that we can't quite see the sun or any planets yet. We will do soon.'

'Do you think we could zoom ahead to day three now, sir?' Alan asks through clenched teeth.

'OK, Alan, don't panic!' says Mr Coles as he turns the dial again. 'Day three is about to begin, everyone. I've speeded things up a little again.'

Doyin asks, 'Sir, are we now three days older than we were before, or how does it work?'

'We are still living by our own time,' answers Mr Coles. 'As I've said before, one of the things the time machine does is to emit a beam that surrounds and protects us. If we keep within this beam, then nothing outside, including distorted time, can affect us. Let's not get into any more detail about this, as that's about as much as I know!'

Within a few seconds it is the beginning of day three. What wonderful things will they witness now?

Chapter 4

A tree for Alan!

'Can we go straight to the creation of the trees, please, Mr Coles?' asks Alan.

'Just a few more moments, Alan,' Mr Coles answers.

'Yeah,' adds Doyin, 'just wait a while.'

'But I've been dying to go now for two days!' shouts Alan.

Everyone laughs. Mr Coles then asks them to be quiet, and, quite mysteriously, they all hear God speak again, each in their own language. 'Let the water below the sky come together in one place, so that the land will appear.'[4]

As soon as they've heard these words, a thunderous sound engulfs them.

Shaheda yells, 'What's happening, sir? Are we still safe?'

Everyone on board is anxious. It sounds like a thousand earthquakes all at once. Mr Coles reassures the class that there is nothing to worry about so long as they stay on the bus.

After a few moments, the minibus, which has been floating on the surface of the ocean, is suddenly elevated way above the water level. Huge land masses are rising out of the sea. As the land begins to form, the waters start to recede into one large ocean. It is an extraordinary sight to behold, and the noise is staggering.

They then hear the Lord speak again: 'The land I shall call "Earth", and the water I shall call "Sea".'[5]

John turns to Mr Coles. 'Has God created all the countries and continents now? I'm only asking because, according to what we've just heard God say, he's created only one piece of land, and one ocean.'

'I think you're right,' answers Mr Coles. 'It would appear that

God has created a "supercontinent" surrounded by one vast ocean. The world in which we live is made up of fragmented land masses from this original "supercontinent"!'

'OK, OK,' interrupts Alan. 'This is all very interesting, but where is my tree?'

'Listen to what God is about to say,' says Mr Coles, looking directly at Alan.

They all hear God speak again. 'Let the earth produce all kinds of plants, those that bear grain and those that bear fruit.'[6]

As soon as the Lord has spoken, the strangest thing happens all round them. It starts to rain, but this is no ordinary rain. It has actually started to rain with seeds! Every type of seed is falling out of the sky and landing on the wet earth. That in itself is totally bizarre, but as soon as the seed lands in the earth, it immediately sprouts into a plant of some sort. There are flowers, shrubs, weeds, trees and every type of foliage imaginable, sprouting up everywhere. One second there is nothing to be seen, and the next there is a 20-metre oak tree before their eyes. It is the strangest thing!

'Wow!' Mr Coles shakes his head in amazement. 'This has got to be one of the most beautiful things I have ever seen.'

'It's like watching one of those nature programmes where they speed up the film of a plant growing,' muses Jilani.

'That's just what I was thinking,' says Natasha. 'I agree with sir, it really is a spectacular sight.'

Alan butts in. 'And the most beautiful thing I can see out there is that huge tree just ahead of us. Can I now go to the toilet, please?'

'Does anyone else need the loo?' asks Mr Coles. 'I'm going to open the minibus door now. There are quite a few trees around us, and they are all inside the protective red beam that the time machine is emitting. When you get outside, you will see the beam ahead of you. Under no circumstances must you step outside it. This is the one and only golden rule of this trip.'

Mr Coles opens the door, and Alan jumps out and runs behind the nearest tree. Some of the others also pop out to stretch their legs. The air smells wonderful, and they all comment on it. What also amazes them is the silence. The seeds have stopped falling; the plants have stopped sprouting. There is no breeze. All the usual background noises have gone—the drone of London traffic, planes flying overhead. Here there is nothing of the kind. It is totally tranquil—or it is until Alan shouts out, 'Ah, that's better!'

'Trust Alan to spoil the peace here,' says Boris.

'You think that's bad,' adds Steven. 'Look at Bronagh! She's walking around with her headphones on, listening to that rubbish rock music of hers.'

They don't stay out too long, as the weather is quite cool. The sun is still hidden by the thick layer of clouds. They will have to wait until day four before they can see the sun, the moon and the stars.

Mr Coles asks them all to get back into the bus, so that they can travel a day forward in time. Everyone teases Alan as he gets back on, asking him whether he's sure he doesn't need to go again.

'Very funny!' is his reply.

'I could have stayed here for ever,' says Doyin. The dreamy way she's looking out of the window shows that she has been really moved by what she has seen. The whole class is in awe at the sight of God's creative power at work.

'I must admit that what we have seen today really is a miracle,' says Sarah suddenly. 'You know, I've never believed in any God or religion, but what's going on all around us is a miracle. I've heard God speak, and I've seen his power. I'm not saying that I'm now a Christian or Muslim or anything, but I know that there is a God. This is all just so cool!'

'You know what?' adds Natasha. 'I'm from a Pentecostal church, and I always believed that my own church and style of worship was the only way to worship God. But what we're seeing here is bigger than anything like that.'

'This experience is going to affect us all in some way,' says Mr Coles. 'I think we should move on to day four now. It's good to be on land at last.'

Chapter 5

Twinkle twinkle little star

Mr Coles goes on, 'Before we move on, could we all open our Bibles again and turn to Genesis chapter 1? Could you please read verses 14 to 19, Boris?'

'OK, sir.'

Then God commanded, 'Let lights appear in the sky to separate day from night and to show the time when days, years, and religious festivals begin; they will shine in the sky to give light to the earth'—and it was done. So God made the two larger lights, the sun to rule over the day and the moon to rule over the night; he also made the stars. He placed the lights in the sky to shine on the earth, to rule over the day and the night, and to separate light from darkness. And God was pleased with what he saw. Evening passed and morning came—that was the fourth day.

'Well read,' says Mr Coles.

'Any time, sir.'

'Right, everyone, I'm going to move some dials here and move us on to the fourth day.' Mr Coles bends down to fiddle with the time machine. 'OK, folks. We're just about there.'

Everyone looks out of the windows. A strong wind begins to blow. It is really overcast outside, but as they look up, the wind starts to clear the sky, which is still quite dark. Alan suddenly shouts out, 'Look up there!' He points into the sky. 'Millions of stars!'

He is right. As the clouds start to move away, they see that there are stars everywhere.

'I've never seen stars so bright, and so many,' gasps Shaheda.

'Has God made those stars just now?' asks Jilani.

'No, I don't believe he has,' answers Mr Coles. 'The Genesis account states, "Let lights appear." I believe that these stars have been there for millions, perhaps billions of years.'

'And remember,' adds John, 'their light has only just reached us on the fourth day, and that on its own shows that these stars have been around for a heck of a long time.'

'And it takes millions and billions of years for light to reach the earth from the stars that are furthest away; I learned that in science!' says Jilani smugly.

'You lot seem to know more than I do when it comes to science,' laughs Mr Coles.

'Not just science, but when it comes to anything,' Bronagh answers cheekily.

They all join in the laughter.

As they continue looking outside, the full moon breaks through the remaining cloud. Because they all live in London, they are normally lucky if they can see a few stars plus the moon. Here they can see everything. It is just so beautiful.

Mr Coles motions to them to be quiet. 'I'm going to move us on by a couple of hours, so that we can see the sun come up. It should be quite a sight!'

'I suppose it'll be the first ever sunrise,' comments Doyin.

'That's right,' nods Mr Coles. 'Remember that the sun has probably been around for millions of years, but because all the clouds and moisture have been blown away, it will now be visible for the first time. Here we go.'

Once again, Mr Coles fiddles with the dial on his time machine. Within a few moments the black sky starts to change to the most amazing, brilliant red.

Steven shouts out, 'Can we get out the bus to see this, sir?'

'Definitely,' says Mr Coles. He is already opening the doors.

They all clamber out. The sight is mesmerizing. They stand and stare, as if in a trance. The beautiful red sky is turning to a spectacularly bright orange colour.

Slowly, on the horizon, in the distant reaches of the ocean, the tip of the mighty sun appears, making its very first appearance on earth. Over the next half hour or so, the giant sun rises in full glory.

Natasha tells the others that her entire body is covered in goose pimples. 'I can't begin to say how amazing this is.'

Even Jilani, so often the class clown, stands there with his mouth wide open as he takes in the enormity of this moment. As the sun continues to rise, class and teacher begin to feel the comforting warmth radiating from the mighty star.

After a while, Mr Coles pops back into the bus and brings out some bottles of water, Coke and lemonade. Bronagh goes around asking who wants what, and helps Mr Coles to pour out the drinks for everyone.

Boris turns to Mr Coles and asks, 'Can we stay here for a while, sir? It's so lovely.' Many of the others agree.

'I'm afraid we have to move on,' answers Mr Coles as he motions to them to get back into the bus. Shaheda helps to collect the empty plastic cups.

Steven asks, 'Sir, if we left our cups behind, do you think that might confuse archaeologists in the future when they come digging here?'

'It's certainly a funny thought,' laughs Mr Coles. 'But that's why we stay inside the protective beam. If you were to leave something here, the beam would automatically destroy it. We are now going to move quickly on to day five. Before we do, everyone please be seated, and then turn back to Genesis chapter 1 verses 20 to 22. Alan, could you read, please?'

Alan pulls a bit of a miserable face, as he hates reading out loud to the class. 'If I have to!'

Then God commanded, 'Let the water be filled with many kinds of living beings, and let the air be filled with birds.' So God created the great sea monsters, all kinds of creatures that live in the water, and all kinds of birds. And God was pleased with what he saw. He blessed them all and told the creatures that live in the water to reproduce, and to fill the sea, and he told the birds to increase in number.

'That was very good, Alan,' smiles Mr Coles. 'You're a great reader.'

The others give him a round of applause, and Alan stands up and gives them all a silly little bow.

Mr Coles does his usual fiddling with the time machine, and they move to the beginning of the fifth day.

Chapter 6

The first bird to dirty a windscreen

'Here we are,' exclaims Mr Coles. 'Day five.' Just as he says this, a large dollop of bird poo splatters right across the windscreen of the minibus.

Mr Coles looks quite shocked. The others howl with laughter.

'This is brilliant,' shouts Alan. 'We are the first to ever see a bird have a cr—'

'Yes, yes,' interrupts Mr Coles.

'The question is, though,' says Doyin, 'how come the bird needed to do a poo? I mean, God has just created the birds, so they can't have had time to even eat yet!'

'Where I live in Mile End,' adds Jilani, 'the pigeons just poo every five seconds, whether they eat or not. It's just what birds do; and it looks like they've been doing that since the very beginning!'

Mr Coles stands up. 'Let's move on from this topic of conversation, shall we? The mess on my windscreen is clear evidence that the birds have now been created. Let's get out for a few moments to take a look.'

'Hope no bird does a whoopsie on me,' laughs Bronagh. They all step outside. It is a wonderful day—blue sky, air fresher than they have ever experienced. And what they can see is magnificent. The trees and the air are full of every type of bird you could imagine. They can see a myriad of striking colours, plumage every colour of the rainbow, on every side.

'This is well cool,' says Natasha.

Mr Coles looks at her. 'You're not wrong.'

Although the bus is now on dry land, the ocean is only a short distance away. As they are all looking up at the trees and the sky, a huge wave suddenly breaks on to the shore. A moment or so later, an enormous whale surfaces right in front of them, blowing a plume of water into the air.

'Wow!' the whole group gasp in unison, half of them leaving their mouths wide open.

'I've only ever seen things like that on nature programmes on Sky TV,' says John.

The group don't know where to look next. The ocean and sky are just alive with activity, and the children are mesmerised.

After a while, Mr Coles tells them that it's time to move on. Many of them complain that they want to stay longer, but he tells them that there's a great deal more to see. They clamber back into the minibus, all talking at once, full of excitement at what they have witnessed. Mr Coles calms them down and prepares them for the following day, day six.

Chapter 7

Good grief! Dinosaurs

'Listen up, folks,' says Mr Coles. 'Everything we have seen so far has been breathtaking, but we've now come to what could be the most spectacular day. God is going to create all the animals and human beings.'

'Wicked!' shouts Jilani. The others laugh excitedly.

Mr Coles continues. 'Soon, we'll all hear God speak in our own language, but before we do, let's read the account from Genesis. Shaheda, could you read for us please?'

'OK, sir.'

Mr Coles asks them to turn to Genesis chapter 1, verses 24 to 31. Shaheda starts to read:

Then God commanded, 'Let the earth produce all kinds of animal life: domestic and wild, large and small'—and it was done. So God made them all, and he was pleased with what he saw.

Then God said, 'And now we will make human beings; they will be like us and resemble us. They will have power over the fish, the birds, and all the animals, domestic and wild, large and small.' So God created human beings, making them to be like himself. He created them male and female, blessed them, and said, 'Have many children, so that your descendants will live all over the earth and bring it under their control. I am putting you in charge of the fish, the birds, and all the wild animals. I have provided all kinds of grain and all kinds of fruit for you to eat; but for all the wild animals and for all the birds I have provided grass and leafy plants for food'—and it was done. God looked at everything he made, and he was very pleased. Evening passed and morning came—that was the sixth day.

'Well read, Shaheda,' Mr Coles smiles at her as she finishes.

'God's always well pleased with what he does, isn't he, sir?' asks Alan.

Mr Coles turns to Alan. 'He certainly is.'

'He creates a perfect world and is pleased,' Natasha says thoughtfully, 'and we go and ruin it all!'

'Humans can be right plonkers, can't they, sir?' says Bronagh.

'You speak for yourself,' laughs Steven.

'You know what I mean, though?' Bronagh continues. 'God creates this most beautiful world, perhaps out of love. He then asks us to look after it—'

'And what do we do?' interrupts John. 'We go and spoil it through war and pollution and greed.'

'Perhaps everyone should be given the chance to travel back in time and witness what we have seen,' says Mr Coles. 'Perhaps it would change people for the better, and we would look after this beautiful creation of God's.'

'No way,' says Doyin. 'People are people, and there's always going to be people who just don't care.'

Boris looks up. 'No one can really say, but I know that the experience of this trip will affect me for the rest of my life. I'll do all I can to work with God's creation and not against it!'

'That was a lovely thing to say!' Natasha responds.

Mr Coles agrees. He then tells them to get ready for the trip to day six. He moves the dial slightly. Night comes, followed by day, all in a matter of a few seconds.

It is another beautiful morning. A blue-turquoise ocean lies ahead. A gentle breeze waves the branches of the trees, and the sound of wonderful birdsong filters into the minibus. The class sit and wait. Then they all hear God speak. He is creating all the animals. Everyone is gazing out of the windows like hawks, waiting to glimpse the first of the animals.

After a few moments of silence, Jilani, the only one looking out of the back window, suddenly yells, 'Let's get out of here! Quick!'

From his voice, the others can tell that he is petrified. When they all scramble to look out of the same window, they immediately realize what's wrong. None of them can believe what they are looking at. About half a mile away, standing near a grove of very tall trees, is a dinosaur.

'Holy Moses!' screams Sarah.

'Are we going to be safe here?' Shaheda asks anxiously. 'Because if anything happens to any of us, you'll find it a little tricky explaining to our parents that we were eaten by a dinosaur!'

Mr Coles immediately reassures them. 'We have nothing to fear. Don't forget that we are surrounded by the protective beam. We have been in a raging ocean and we were perfectly safe. We can even step out of the bus now, and as long as we remain within the protection of the beam, we'll be fine.'

Boris is the first to pluck up the courage to step outside. He stares over at the dinosaur, completely dumbfounded. Bronagh emerges from the bus behind him and says, 'This is what it must have felt like for those people in that film *Jurassic Park* when they first saw the dinosaurs.'

'Don't mention *Jurassic Park*,' says Steven, half-joking and half-petrified. 'In that film there were crazy dinosaurs chasing everyone and trying to eat them!'

Eventually they all get out. As they stand and watch, dinosaurs begin to appear everywhere. But it isn't just dinosaurs. They see cats and dogs running around, and hippos wallowing in a nearby lake. There are lions and elephants wandering past. What is quite amazing, though, is that they are all eating either grass or leaves from trees and bushes, even the lions.

'This isn't right,' whispers Alan. 'Why are they all eating grass? Those cows over there are eating grass. I understand that. But what about those lions, or some of those huge dinosaurs?'

'Well, the Bible makes it very clear in Genesis 1 verse 30, which we read a few moments ago,' responds Mr Coles. 'All the animals are to eat grass and leaves.'

Natasha nods her head. 'The pastor at my church says that this is the way it was in the beginning. He says that before sin came into the world, all animals and Adam and Eve lived side by side. It was Paradise. He says that everything and everyone were vegetarians to begin with.'

'I've heard many Christians say that too,' says Mr Coles, looking quite thoughtful.

'I read about it in some Muslim book as well,' adds Jilani.

They fall silent again for a while, many of the class wandering around within the beam, just staring at the wonders surrounding them.

John walks over to Mr Coles, a puzzled frown on his face. 'Sir,' he begins. 'I've always been led to believe that dinosaurs lived millions of years ago.' The others gather around, clearly thinking about the same thing. John continues. 'And there isn't any mention of dinosaurs in the Bible. Hasn't carbon dating proved that the dinosaur bones that have been discovered are millions of years old?'

'Yes, sir,' Alan joins in. 'Why aren't dinosaurs mentioned in the Bible?'

'These are brilliant questions, and I can only say that I am as amazed as you lot here,' says Mr Coles, scratching his head. 'We now know the truth, and the only thing I can tell you is that there are many Christians who believe that God created dinosaurs on day six, as we have witnessed here.'

'What's their argument to back that up?' asks John.

'I can help you answer that if you want,' Natasha offers. 'My church has always taught this. My pastor says that sometimes Christians are tempted to change the Bible, just so that they can fit their theories based on science. But we are taught that scientific theories are changing all the time, but the word of God never changes. My pastor says that when Christians try to change what is written in Genesis, he always quotes the following verse to them: 'Were you there when I made the world?'[7]

'Nice response,' laughs Bronagh.

'And an excellent argument,' acknowledges Mr Coles. 'Quite simply, no scientist was ever there at the very beginning, so any theories they have will never be more than educated guesses.'

'That's right, sir,' adds Natasha. 'The only one we should believe is the one who was there at the beginning, and that's God.'

'Wow, Natasha,' Steven grins. 'You're on a roll!'

Boris adds, 'It looks as if God has created dinosaurs to live peacefully with human beings.'

Bronagh nods. 'And all the animals here seem to be living peacefully with each other. They're plodding around quite happy, nibbling grass here and a few leaves there.'

John turns back to Mr Coles. 'So what about all this scientific evidence claiming that dinosaurs lived millions of years ago?'

'Well,' answers Mr Coles, 'there are many people who believe that there is no real scientific evidence to prove it. Some folk argue that the actual physical evidence contradicts the very idea that these beasts lived millions of years ago. Apparently, dinosaur bones are not carbon dated. What happens is that the bones are simply assigned an age based on how old a scientist thinks they might be.'

'I heard someone in my local mosque say something similar,' says Shaheda. 'I heard that there have been some bones carbon dated, and that they were found to be thousands of years old, not millions like the scientists thought.'

'Well,' Steven shrugs, 'the fact is, there are dinosaurs here, and they were created on the sixth day.'

As they are discussing this, a huge brachiosaurus starts to make its way towards them. Alan shouts, 'Amazing, it's coming towards us! Look at the size of that!'

There is no disputing it. The beast is absolutely massive—about 20 metres tall.

'Sir,' whispers Doyin, not wanting the dinosaur to hear. 'I hope that beam thing really does protect us.'

'Don't worry,' says Mr Coles calmly. 'It has done so far, and it will now.' He is right. The beast comes right up to the edge of the beam, a few metres away from them. It then comes to a halt. The whole group stare up at it with eyes wide and mouths open.

What they see next really terrifies them—a tyrannosaurus rex! It too is making its way towards them, looking exactly like the bloodthirsty monster in *Jurassic Park*. Again, Mr Coles intervenes to calm down the class, saying, 'This is Paradise, everyone. We've already established that every living creature here is a vegetarian. There is no violence or killing. I expect that only happens when sin enters the world.'

Mr Coles is right. The T-Rex lumbers up to the brachiosaurus. Both animals look at each other quite peacefully, and then walk off in different directions.

'Amazing,' gasps John. 'No one is going to believe us when we tell them what we have seen.'

'We won't be telling anyone,' says Mr Coles. 'They just won't believe us. We'll talk more about this at the end of the trip, just before we get back to school.'

'Sir's right,' Bronagh agrees. 'If we tell anyone, they'll only think that we're mad. Let's tell them we went to visit some old country churches or something.'

Mr Coles nods. 'Good idea!'

Alan then asks, 'Sir, why aren't there any dinosaurs in the Bible?'

'Good question,' adds Boris.

'That certainly is a good question,' Mr Coles replies. 'The actual word "dinosaur" is not found in the Bible because it was not invented until some time in the 1800s. But that doesn't mean anything. Many Christians do believe that dinosaurs are in the Bible, but they are just given a different name. We are told in the Bible— and we will read this later—that Adam was the one who named all the animals.'

'That's what I learned in church, sir,' Natasha says eagerly. 'Didn't Adam call dinosaurs behe... beha.. Oh, I can't remember!'

'You're almost right.' says Mr Coles. 'The name in Hebrew is behemoth.'

'I knew it began with a B!' exclaims Natasha.

'Sounds like they teach you a lot in your church,' comments Alan. 'It seems to be true as well.'

Boris tells the group that he once heard on TV that the word 'dinosaur' actually meant a 'terrible lizard'.

'They don't seem that terrible to me—just terribly big!' says Steven. They all laugh.

'So where are dinosaurs mentioned in the Bible, then, sir?' asks Jilani after a pause.

Mr Coles goes back into the bus to collect the Bibles. He hands them out, and the class sit down on the grass. It's an incredible sight: this small group on a school trip, sitting outside at the beginning of time, surrounded by dinosaurs, lions and every animal imaginable. Beyond them, the beautiful new ocean crashes on the new shore, the waves alive with whales and other sea creatures. It is truly spectacular.

'OK, I'd like to answer Jilani's question,' says Mr Coles. 'Could you all please turn to the book of Job.'

They flick through the pages, and eventually get there.

'In this book, we find the word "behemoth" being used to describe the largest of the animals that God has created. This Hebrew word actually means "giant" or "kingly beast". What is interesting is that, in the Bible, there are many animals that we can clearly recognise, because the Hebrew name for them has been translated into English. But when the people who turned the Bible into English came to the word "behemoth", they had no idea how to translate it, because there was no animal in the world that fitted the description. But Job would have seen this animal himself, as it was created alongside humans.'

Mr Coles asks the class to turn to chapter 39, and they read through all the verses. He explains to them that God starts by telling Job about all the small animals that he made, before turning to the larger animals.

'And now we get to the crucial verses which will answer Jilani's question,' Mr Coles continues. 'Bronagh, could you please read Job chapter 40, from verse 15, until I ask you to stop?'

'No problem,' she replies.

Look at the monster Behemoth; I created him and I created you. He eats grass like a cow, but what strength there is in his body, and what power there is in his muscles! His tail stands up like a cedar, and the muscles in his legs are strong. His bones are as strong as bronze, and his legs are like iron bars.'[8]

'Thanks, Bronagh, you can hold it there,' says Mr Coles.

'So why do you think that's a dinosaur, sir?' asks John. 'We read this in my church once, and I was told that Behemoth was probably just a hippo, or maybe an elephant.'

'That is what many people think,' answers Mr Coles. 'But others argue that people who think it is just referring to a hippo or elephant are ignoring the actual description given in God's word. Let me ask you all a question. What sort of tails do hippos and elephants have? In fact, have a quick look over there.' Mr Coles stands up and points at a group of elephants wandering between them and the ocean. 'Look at their tails. Someone tell me what their tails look like.'

'They've hardly got a tail,' laughs Alan.

'Exactly! That's the point.' Mr Coles points them all to verse 17: '"His tail stands up like a cedar." This is the key verse. We have just agreed that elephants and hippos have the tiniest of tails. But in the verse here, the behemoth has a tail so long and powerful that God compares it to a cedar tree, one of the largest trees in the ancient world. The tail of this creature was as long and thick as a tree trunk. We know of no living creature that has a tail like that.'

'I've seen pictures of a diplodocus,' adds Boris, 'and its tail was enormous. If I had to describe that tail, then comparing it to a tree would probably be very accurate.'

John looks round the group. 'I once thought that the behemoth was just a hippo or elephant, but looking around now, on the sixth day of creation, it's obvious that it means these massive creatures. No wonder they're described in the book of Job as 'the most amazing of all my creatures".'[9] He shakes his head. 'This is all just so unbelievable.'

'It's fantastic,' Mr Coles agrees. 'Not in a million years would I have thought I'd see something like this.' He looks over to where a large lake is shimmering in the distance, and points it out to the others. 'Watch that brachiosaurus walking into the lake.'

One of the huge beasts is slowly wading in. Before long, the only part still visible is its enormous head.

'That lake must have risen by a few inches,' laughs Bronagh.

'I think you're right,' says Jilani.

Mr Coles then says, 'Can you all look in the book of Job again, chapter 40? That huge beast over there helps to explain a few of the other verses in this book. In verse 21 it says, "He hides among the reeds in the swamp." Although what we can see over there is a lake, it's covered with reeds and other plant life. That dinosaur is doing exactly what this verse states.'

'You're right, sir,' says Boris. 'It's over there, hiding among the reeds.'

'Hey, sir, sir!' shrieks Doyin, really excited. 'Look at verses 23 and 24 as well. I think this applies to the dinosaur too.'

They all quickly read through these verses, some of them mumbling aloud as they do so.

'I think she's right,' laughs Mr Coles. 'Hey, Alan, could you read those verses out for us?'

'Yeah, all right.'

He is not afraid of a rushing river; he is calm when the Jordan dashes in his face. Who can blind his eyes and capture him? Or who can catch his snout in a trap?

'Thanks for that, Alan.' Mr Coles proceeds to ask the class why these verses might also apply to dinosaurs. Doyin obviously knows, so he tells her not to say anything.

Natasha puts up her hand. 'I think I might know why. Is it because the dinosaur's so huge and powerful, and no river or rushing water will ever be able to scare it or even move it?'

Mr Coles nods. 'I think that's exactly it. Well done!'

'Cheers, sir,' smiles Natasha. She loves a bit of praise!

Mr Coles continues, 'Verse 24 talks about traps being set to try to capture this dinosaur. Impossible! As it says in verse 19, this really is the most amazing of all God's creatures, and only God could defeat this beast. Let's take another look at the brachiosaurus. What can you see of that creature at the moment?'

'Just its head, eyes and nose,' shout many of the class.

'Well done,' replies Mr Coles. 'In verse 24, the eyes and nose are mentioned, and I think this is a very important point. We saw this creature on the land a minute ago, and now it's wallowing in the water, and all we can see are its eyes and nose. This verse really must be referring to the dinosaur we are looking at.'

John adds, 'I saw on a documentary about dinosaurs that some could totally submerge their bodies in water, with only their eyes and nose showing. Look, its nose is actually on the top of its head, different from other animals.'

'Wow,' gasps Natasha, 'and that's what verse 24 says: who can capture his snout in a trap? It's impossible!'

Mr Coles asks them all to gather around again and sit on the grass. When they go silent, he says, 'God was telling Job to be amazed or to "behold" this marvellous creature. Job must have seen one before. These animals were alive when Job was, so it would seem that dinosaurs and human beings were equally part of God's creation. God wanted to make Job aware of his mighty power.'

'He certainly did that, sir, by showing Job one of these monsters,' laughs Jilani.

'That's right,' nods Mr Coles.

Natasha then opens her eyes wide, and smiles like a Cheshire cat. 'I've just thought about something, sir.'

'Go on,' Mr Coles acknowledges.

'Well, sir,' Natasha says. 'Some people sometimes say that the Bible is rubbish and that the creation stories are just not true. They always use the dinosaur as their evidence. I reckon that the devil uses the dinosaur to confuse people about the truth in Genesis.'

'Go Natasha, go Natasha,' some of the others chant, realizing that she is really getting going in this debate.

'Thank you, fans!' she responds, laughing.

'Hey, let's not interrupt her,' says Mr Coles. 'She's doing well.'

Natasha continues, 'Thanks, sir. Now, where was I? Oh yeah, the devil uses the dinosaur as a tool to make people not turn to God. I reckon that God must have known that the devil or Satan would try to deceive people. The devil wants people to think that all life on earth evolved over millions or billions of years.'

'Or trillions,' laughs Alan.

'I think we get the point,' says Mr Coles. 'Please continue.'

'Well, that's pretty much it, sir. I think that God must have known that one day dinosaurs would become extinct, and that people like Ross in *Friends* would come along and dig up these bones.'

'I love *Friends*,' shouts Alan. 'I think the girl who plays Rachel is really—'

'That's enough,' says Mr Coles.

'Anyway, sir,' continues Natasha, 'God knew that these bones were going to be dug up, and that they would confuse people. That's why God tells us all about dinosaurs in the book of Job.'

'That really is brilliant!' says Mr Coles, looking almost bemused at her line of argument. 'You certainly have your moments of inspiration.'

'I know,' laughs Natasha.

'Now look who's the professor,' shouts Jilani. The others laugh.

'I have to admit,' says Doyin, 'that's one of the arguments I always used to use for not believing in God, and now that Natasha has put it like that, perhaps the devil does use the dinosaur argument as a tool to prevent people believing in God.'

'Alleluia!' shouts Natasha.

'Is it lunch-time yet, sir?' asks Alan.

'We're having a great discussion about dinosaurs and evolution,' laughs Bronagh, 'and all you can think about is your belly.' Some of them look over at Alan, and start snorting like pigs.

Mr Coles looks at his watch. 'We've travelled back in time more years than we can count; we've witnessed the creation of the world, plants and animals; and it's only half past eleven!'

'You're right,' shouts Steven. 'How bizarre is that?'

'So what you're saying,' moans Alan, 'is that it isn't lunch-time yet?'

Mr Coles tells him that they'll eat their lunch in about an hour's time. Bronagh offers Alan a packet of crisps. 'Oh, cheers!' Alan says, a big smile on his face.

'Right, folks,' says Mr Coles, 'I'd like you to get back on the minibus now. We are about to witness the most exciting part of God's creation, the making of Adam and Eve.'

'Cool!' shouts Doyin. They all clamber back on the bus, full of fresh excitement.

Alan asks Mr Coles, 'Sir, will they be naked, like it says in the Bible?' Some of the others snigger at this. Before they set off, they spend another five minutes just staring out of the windows, watching the dinosaurs. It has all been so much to take in. Mr Coles rouses them by saying that he's about to programme the next destination into the time machine.

But Boris asks suddenly, 'Sir, we've seen that these dinosaurs were created at the same time as human beings, so when did they suddenly disappear, or become extinct?'

'A good question,' Mr Coles replies. 'I think that will have to be something we find out for ourselves, if we have time for it.'

'It could have been the flood,' says Steven. 'I think I might have heard someone at my church say that.'

'It may well have been the flood,' Mr Coles answers. 'Let's hope we get long enough to find out for ourselves.'

'But can't we make time with the time machine?' Jilani interrupts. 'We can go back to school as if we're about to set off on the trip again, and then we won't have used up any time.'

The others look confused at this suggestion.

'An interesting thought,' laughs Mr Coles, 'but let's not complicate things. I'm going by the time on my watch, and I will be aiming to get back to school at about four in the afternoon, as it said on the letter you took home to your parents. Let's not get into a discussion about time travel again.'

'You're right, sir, it's just too mind-boggling,' says Bronagh.

Mr Coles then types into the control device: 'The garden of Eden—Adam and Eve.'

Chapter 8

Adam and Eve

'OK, everyone,' says Mr Coles, turning round to face them all. 'This is the spot.'

As they look out of the window, they are overwhelmed at what they see. It is so beautiful!

'Wow!' says Jilani. 'This is how I imagine paradise to be.'

'You're right, Jilani,' adds Shaheda. 'This is how the Qur'an describes paradise.'

It is the garden of Eden, but it's not just a beautiful garden. The only accurate word to describe it is 'heavenly'. The flowers are perfect. The trees are magnificent. Many of them are fruit-bearing, and wherever the class look they see the juiciest apples, oranges and pears imaginable. And that's just the fruit they recognize!

'Sir,' says John, 'we have got to eat our packed lunches here. It's incredible.'

'You know, sir,' says Natasha, 'it's not just that this place looks so heavenly. What's really special is how it feels to be here.'

Everyone agrees with her.

Mr Coles adds, 'You're exactly right, Natasha. I feel that I don't have a worry in the world. It's all so tranquil.'

Alan announces that he has goosepimples, and Bronagh says the same. 'Why are we feeling like this? I'm just at peace with the whole world.'

'We really are in paradise,' says Doyin softly.

Mr Coles stands up and opens the door of the minibus. One by one the class jump out. Nobody says a word. The smell outside is also heavenly—the fragrance of flowers and fruit is so sweet. Just ahead of them is a stream. The sound of the water trickling is wonderfully soothing. Doyin starts to cry a little as she stands there trying to take it all in. Bronagh asks if she's OK.

'I'm fine, thanks, Bronagh. I'm just so overwhelmed. Living in East London, and having parents who argue all the time, I hardly ever get moments of calm like this. Standing here in what must be paradise—it's just incredible.'

Mr Coles asks them to take a seat on the lush green grass. They sit down and no one speaks for quite a while. They feel at peace with each other and with the whole world. No one wants to ruin the moment by talking.

Somewhere in the distance, they hear the roar of a dinosaur. None of them are startled. This is paradise. There is no fear, because all the animals live in peace as well, even the dinosaurs.

As they look round the huge garden, they notice that in the middle, a few hundred metres away, there stands a tree far bigger and mightier than any other tree in the garden. It is a fruit tree, perhaps apple or pear; they can't quite make it out from where they sit.

'Hey, sir,' asks Boris, 'you don't think that's the tree that Adam and Eve were told not to pick any fruit from?'

As they check out the tree, a brilliant white light appears about 400 metres in front of them.

'What on earth is that, sir?' asks Doyin.

'It must be something to do with God,' answers Natasha. 'God usually appears as a light to people.'

Mr Coles looks at Natasha. 'I think you're right. I also think that we're about to witness the creation of Adam.'

'Sir,' asks Jilani, 'do you think God knows we're here? And if he does, won't he mind?'

'Blimey,' laughs Mr Coles, 'that's a tricky one. The only thing I can think of is that God knows everything—past, present and future. He must know we're here, and if he didn't want us here, we would know by now. I really wish you'd stop asking me these tricky questions about time travel!'

'Just keeping you on your toes, sir,' jokes Jilani.

'Sir, sir, look over there at the light!' screams Alan. They all turn round. What they see is soil rising up from the ground. It isn't just being blown by the wind, and it isn't just a random movement of the soil. It is deliberately being manipulated. Slowly, in front of their eyes, they see the soil being shaped into a man. It is unbelievable.

'The first human being,' Bronagh says in an awestruck whisper.

They all get to their feet and stand together, staring. And then, all at once, the act of creation is complete. In front of the light, there now stands a naked man. There is no life in him, though, no sign of breathing or movement of any kind. One or two of the girls look away. Mr Coles tells the group not to be embarrassed. He reminds them that they have all sat in sex education lessons over the past few years, and seeing Adam naked here, in the garden of Eden, is totally natural.

Jilani and Shaheda keep looking away, though. Muslims are not supposed to see anyone naked, and to them, Adam is the first prophet on earth. Mr Coles tells them that he understands their respectful gesture.

All the others keep their eyes fixed on the bright light and the lifeless man in front of it.

'Can you hear that?' Boris says suddenly.

'What?' most of the others respond at once.

'It sounds like the wind blowing.'

'It must be God's life-giving breath!' gasps Natasha.

'Well done,' says Mr Coles. 'Genesis chapter 2, verse 7 says, "Then the Lord God took some soil from the ground and formed a man out of it; he breathed life-giving breath into his nostrils and the man began to live."'

After another few seconds, the event that they have all been waiting for happens. The figure in front of them slowly opens his eyes. Immediately he smiles and starts to move his arms and legs. He looks around him. You can see him breathing in the fresh, sweet-smelling air. He seems full of happiness and contentment.

The bright light then moves towards the middle of the beautiful garden, and the man follows it.

As he comes closer and closer, the girls start to giggle a little, but they continue to watch him, fascinated.

'How weird!' Natasha says suddenly.

'What do you mean?' asks Mr Coles.

'His colour. I can't quite work out what colour he is.'

'You're right,' adds Bronagh. 'At times he looks white, then a shade of brown. I just can't make it out.'

'It's like looking at one of those cars sprayed with that strange metallic paint,' says John. 'The colour seems to change every second, depending how the light reflects it.'

'That's a brilliant comparison,' Mr Coles replies, impressed. Jilani turns round to have a brief look.

'Wow!' he says. 'That man is all of our colours.'

'We're all descended from this man,' says Doyin. 'So it makes sense that he isn't just one colour. Jilani's right—he's all of our colours.'

'It's a perfect example of how we really are all equal,' adds Bronagh.

The light leads the man right into the middle of the beautiful garden. The light then begins to shine even brighter. Once again they all hear God's voice, speaking in their own language.

You may eat the fruit of any tree in the garden, except the tree that gives knowledge of what is good and what is bad. You must not eat the fruit of that tree; if you do, you will die the same day.[10]

'It's just as it's written in Genesis,' exclaims John.

'Why did God go and have to say that to the man?' asks Alan.

'Say what, exactly?' Mr Coles replies.

'All that stuff about not eating the fruit from that one tree,' Alan goes on. 'Now that he's been told not to do something, of course he's bloomin' well going to go and do it, isn't he?'

'Sounds just like you, Alan!' laughs Bronagh.

'That's what I mean,' Alan says. 'Sometimes, when teachers tell me not to do something, I go and do it anyway, just to annoy them!'

'At least you're being honest,' Mr Coles grins.

Sarah then speaks up, having not said a great deal so far. 'I think you once told us in an RE lesson, sir, that this is all to do with "free will" or something.'

'What are you on about?' Jilani turns to her.

Sarah continues, 'Mr Coles taught us that the greatest gift God gave to people was the gift of free will.'

'I remember that lesson, too,' says Doyin. 'If we weren't given that gift of free will, we would just be like robots.'

'That's right,' adds Sarah. 'We would have been programmed to do good, exactly like a robot.'

'Well done, you lot,' says Mr Coles. 'So you do pay attention in my lessons!' They all laugh.

He continues, 'You're right. We have been given the gift of free will. We can choose. Having that choice is what really makes us human.'

'Hey, look what's happening now!' interrupts Alan.

They all look over to where Alan is pointing. The man, Adam, has sat himself down on a rock. The shining light is still behind him, and in front of him is a queue of animals stretching away as far as they can see.

Mr Coles asks them to turn quickly to Genesis chapter 2, verses 18 to 20. 'Sarah, could you read, please?'

Sarah reads slowly and clearly:

Then the Lord God said, 'It is not good for the man to live alone. I will make a suitable companion to help him.' So he took some soil from the ground and formed all the animals and all the birds. Then he brought them to the man to see what he would name them; and that is how they all got their names. So the man named all the birds and all the animals; but not one of them was a suitable companion to help him.

Mr Coles explains that what is happening now is that Adam is naming all the animals. It is spectacular to watch. Every conceivable type of animal is in that queue, from the largest dinosaurs to the tiniest insects. The class stand in silence, once again overwhelmed by what they are witnessing.

Adam seems to be making quick work of the naming. But then the dogs come to the front of the queue. Adam appears to hesitate for a while. He grins as he looks at the dogs, leaping up at him, tails wagging hard. Adam turns and smiles up at the shining light of God. Adam seems to be saying that he wants these animals to be his closest companions.

'Even here at the beginning of creation, it seems that the dog really is man's best friend,' says Mr Coles.

'But Adam won't choose the dog, sir,' says Bronagh.

'I know, but he's obviously thinking about it for a few seconds.'

Mr Coles suggests that sitting here in the garden of Eden, watching Adam name all the animals, would be a perfect time to eat their packed lunches.

'Thank God for that!' shouts Alan.

'Go on then, Alan,' laughs Natasha. 'There's God over there in that bright light!'

'Let's just be careful with what we say around here,' says Mr Coles quietly.

He asks John and Boris to get the box of packed lunches from the bus. Alan helps out as well, desperate to get his hands on some food. The bags of food are shared round.

Steven comments that it might be a good idea to say a little prayer in thanks for the food, seeing as God isn't too far away.

'Good idea,' Mr Coles replies. 'Natasha, could you say grace please?'

Instead of bowing their heads, they decide to look over at the shining light. It seems the right thing to do while giving thanks for the food.

'For what we are about to receive, may the Lord make us truly thankful.'

'Amen,' they all say.

They tuck into their sandwiches, crisps and fruit. No one says much. It is simply extraordinary to be sitting there, eating their lunch and watching all the animals pass by.

When they have finished eating, Mr Coles asks them to clear up thoroughly. He then suggests that they all get back on the bus and go forward in time a little to get to the creation of Eve.

'Oh yeah,' laughs Alan. 'Can't wait to see her!'

'You and your rude little mind,' says Doyin.

'OK, everyone, calm down,' says Mr Coles. He fiddles with the dial on the machine, and a moment or so later he calls out, 'We're here!'

They all climb out of the bus again. They are still in the beautiful garden, and Adam is still sitting on the rock, but the animals have gone. Before anything else happens, Mr Coles passes around the Bibles. He asks them to turn to Genesis chapter 2, verses 21 to 23, and suggests that John read aloud for them. John clears his throat.

Then the Lord God made the man fall into a deep sleep, and while he was sleeping, he took out one of the man's ribs and closed up the flesh. He formed a woman out of the rib and brought her to him. Then the man said, 'At last, here is one of my own kind—Bone taken from my bone, and flesh from my flesh. "Woman" is her name because she was taken out of man.'

'Thank you, John, that was well read.'

Mr Coles asks them to keep looking at Adam and the bright light. They all face in that direction. After a few moments, they notice Adam getting up from the rock, walking towards a patch of lush grass, and lying down. The bright light follows him. Very soon, he falls into a deep sleep.

'Oh no! I hate the sight of blood!' says Doyin through clenched teeth.

'I think it's great,' shouts Steven.

As they watch, it is suddenly as if a surgeon has made a large incision in Adam's side. It looks quite gory, and the rest of the class can understand Doyin's outburst! The incision is bad enough, but when they see a rib being removed from Adam's side, most of the class turn pale and look away. After the rib has been taken out of Adam's side, the incision in his side mysteriously disappears. There isn't even a scar.

'That was like something out of *Star Trek*,' says John slowly. 'The way that incision just totally disappeared!'

'*Star Trek*'s boring,' says Shaheda.

'No it isn't,' says Alan, joining in the argument.

'This is no time to debate who does and who doesn't like *Star Trek*,' interrupts Mr Coles. 'Look out of the window now.'

They all do as Mr Coles says—and gasp in astonishment. Just as it was with the creation of Adam, they notice the soil blowing around the rib, which is somehow suspended in mid-air. After a few moments, the soil begins to take shape.

'Wow!' says Steven. 'That is one fit woman!'

'I know,' adds Alan. 'Look at the size of her—'

'That's enough of that,' says Mr Coles.

'She really is quite beautiful,' says Bronagh.

The beautiful woman stands over Adam, who is still in a deep sleep. She lightly touches his face.

Adam begins to stir. When he sees the woman standing over him, his wide smile shows that he is very impressed and extremely happy! He stands up and holds her hands, and they hear him speaking. Just as with God's voice, they each hear him use their own language. Perhaps it's a side-effect of the time machine's protective beam around the minibus.

At last, here is one of my own kind—Bone taken from my bone, and flesh from my flesh. 'Woman' is her name because she was taken out of man.[11]

'It's hard to tell what colour she is, as well,' says Boris. 'She seems to have no colour and yet all colours.'

'This is quite amazing,' Bronagh says to Mr Coles. 'Here we are, looking at the first two human beings on the planet!'

Natasha says, 'In a way, sir, these two people are our great-great-great-great-times millions-grandparents!'

'According to Islam, we are descended from these two people,' remarks Jilani. 'According to Christianity as well,' adds Doyin.

'Sometimes I think there are more similarities between our two religions than there are differences.'

'A good observation,' says Mr Coles.

Steven and Alan start to giggle a little, as they both have their eyes glued to the naked woman standing in front of them.

'Boys will be boys,' says Bronagh, looking over at them, knowing full well what they are sniggering about.

'Don't know why you're staring at us like that, Bronagh,' replies Alan. 'We noticed how some of the girls had their eyes fixed on Adam's—'

'That's enough, folks,' Mr Coles stops their conversation going any further.

'But sir,' says Alan, trying to justify himself. 'How can they just walk around with nothing on? It's not normal.'

Natasha answers the question. 'I was taught at church that Adam and Eve weren't embarrassed to walk around naked, because right now there is no sin or evil in the world. At this moment in time, they are perfect, totally happy and natural, and living in paradise.'

'Oh my word,' says Steven. 'It is true!'

'What?' they all shout.

'Adam and Eve don't have belly buttons!'

They all focus on Adam and Eve. It is true—no navels!

'Why's that, then?' asks Alan.

'I think it's quite obvious,' says Mr Coles. 'You need to remember that our navels are simply scars formed from the attachment of the umbilical cord to our mothers. Once we were born, this cord was cut, and eventually the stump dropped off to form our belly buttons. Adam and Eve were not born to any woman, so why would they have belly buttons?'

'It's seems so obvious now that you've explained it, sir,' says Bronagh. 'And of course any children that they have are going to have navels.'

'That's right,' Mr Coles agrees.

'They'll be a good laugh at a party,' grins Alan, 'showing people that they have no navels!'

'Actually,' says Doyin, 'I think they'll be quite proud of themselves. They can tell people that they were the first two humans on the planet, and they'll be able to prove it!'

They all look at Adam and Eve. Adam has now truly found his closest companion. They really are the first happy couple.

John then asks, 'So are these two the first married couple, sir?'

'That's a good question,' Mr Coles replies. 'In Matthew's Gospel, Jesus reminds people that the real meaning of marriage is based on the first ever marriage, and the first ever marriage is between Adam and Eve.' He turns in his Bible to the New Testament.

Jesus answered, 'Haven't you read the scripture that says that in the beginning the Creator made people male and female? And God said, "For this reason a man will leave his father and mother and unite with his wife, and the two will become one." So they are no longer two, but one. No human being must separate, then, what God has joined together.'[12]

'I reckon Adam's really lucky, sir,' says Alan.

'Why?' asks Mr Coles, sensing that there may be a silly reply coming up.

'Because he is the only man ever not to have a mother-in-law!'

They all laugh at this. It's funny, but also quite true.

The two naked figures walk away hand in hand, stopping sometimes to reach up for a piece of fruit. They are a picture of bliss.

Jilani suddenly blurts out, 'I reckon that Adam must have been a really brainy bloke!'

'Why do you suddenly say that?' asks Natasha.

'Well for a start, he can speak! It took us lot quite a few years before we could speak. Once he'd been created, he could speak straight away and understand things. I'd call that pretty brainy.'

'I think he's right,' adds Boris. 'Adam also named all those animals in a really short time.'

'And he remembered them all,' says Doyin.

'I think you're correct,' says Mr Coles. 'He really is quite a brainy chap.'

'He might be real brainy,' laughs Steven, 'but he's still walking around in the nude! There's nothing clever about that!'

The others laugh.

'I think there is something in what Jilani says, you know,' ponders John. 'Adam and Eve could possibly be the two most intelligent people that ever lived. They have been created as two perfect human beings. Think of geniuses, people like Einstein, or Beethoven.'

'Don't forget the women as well,' Natasha adds.

'Name a woman genius like those two, then,' laughs Alan.

'Only in science last week, we did about Marie Curie who discovered radium. So there you are!' Natasha snaps back.

'Keep your hair on,' Alan replies.

John continues with the point he is trying to make. 'I think we can get a slight idea of what Adam and Eve must have been like if we think of other brilliant people in history. Put them all together, and you get Adam and Eve.'

'Interesting point,' acknowledges Mr Coles.

Boris tells the group to look at Adam and Eve again, as they are now walking off into the distance. Soon they are out of sight.

'I think we'll move on now,' says Mr Coles.

'Are we going to see how sin came into the world?' asks Doyin.

'I'm not sure if I want to see that,' says John.

'I don't like the idea of that either,' Shaheda agrees.

The rest of the class insist that they do want to see this crucial moment in time.

'I'll understand if some people don't want to watch,' Mr Coles assures them.

'Maybe we can run out and stop Eve taking the fruit,' suggests Alan.

'Don't be so stupid,' says Bronagh. 'We can't alter history. Besides, if it were any one of us out there, I'm sure that we would also sin at some stage.'

'Only because Eve sinned first,' shouts Alan.

'Let's not complicate things here,' says Mr Coles. 'Bronagh is quite correct. We can't go out there and change history. If we did, we'd probably cease to exist. The greatest gift that God has given us all is the gift of free will. We can make choices. Adam and Eve were also given this wonderful gift. If we didn't possess the gift of free will, what do you think we'd be like?'

'We'd be like robots,' answers Bronagh.

'Exactly,' says Mr Coles, giving Bronagh the thumbs up. 'I'm just going to move the dial to get us to the point where Adam and Eve sin against God.' And within a few moments, they are there.

Chapter 9

The first sinner

Mr Coles asks everybody to step out of the bus. They do so, and flop down on the grass to wait. Not long after, they glimpse Eve strolling through the garden, looking happy and peaceful.

'It's such a shame seeing her so content, and knowing what is about to happen,' sighs Bronagh.

No one replies. It's quite obvious from the worried expressions on their faces that everyone is thinking more or less the same thing. Eve is standing quite close to the tree that gives knowledge of what is good and bad.

'Sir,' says Alan suddenly. 'What was the point of God creating this tree in the first place? If he'd just left it out, Adam and Eve would never have got into any trouble.'

'That's a good point,' says Bronagh.

They all look at Mr Coles for some words of wisdom. Mr Coles stares at the grass a moment, obviously wondering how to answer.

'I believe that God is extremely generous,' he says at last. 'He has made it clear that Adam and Eve can eat anything they want, from the many trees and bushes he has created. Out of all these sources of food that God has created, he asks Adam to leave just one tree alone. I believe that this tree is a symbol, a reminder that God is the creator. To put it simply, the tree shows that God is the boss.'

Bronagh says thoughtfully, 'In a way, sir, it's a bit like a sacrament.'

'What's one of them when it's at home?' asks Jilani.

'Our priest says that a sacrament is an "outward visible sign of an inward invisible grace",' Bronagh replies carefully. 'Here, the outward sign that we can see is the tree, and the inward meaning of looking at the tree is that it represents God.'

'Nice one, Professor Bronagh,' laughs Jilani. The others look impressed.

'That was brilliantly explained, Bronagh. Well done!' says Mr Coles. 'Every time Adam and Eve look at this tree, they should be reminded that God is their creator, and that they are to obey him. By regularly coming to this tree, they should think about God's greatness and goodness, and each time they come, they should get to know and understand God a little more. It should be a great blessing for them both.'

'If they eat the fruit, then, sir, will they be rebelling against God?' asks Sarah.

'Well done, Sarah,' says Mr Coles, pleased with her insight. 'As Sarah quite rightly says, by eating this fruit they will clearly be rebelling against God. They will then experience evil, and that will be the awful moment when all humankind will know evil as well as good.'

'Is there something supernatural about the fruit on that tree?' asks Alan.

'Not at all,' Mr Coles replies. 'The fruit is no more delicious than any other fruit in this beautiful place. It's all about Adam and Eve deciding to rebel against God, and then sensing evil for the first time.'

The whole class fall silent, and look at Eve standing next to the tree. Then they see that in front of her is a huge python. No one in the group panics, as all the animals they have seen so far, including dinosaurs, lions and tigers, have been peaceful herbivores. The snake has crawled right up to Eve, and is staring into her eyes. Its stare is obviously quite hypnotic, as Eve can't take her eyes off the creature. It is almost as if she is in some sort of trance.

It is then that the whole class hear the most evil and sinister of voices, and once again they can all hear this voice speaking in their own language. The snake asks Eve, 'Did God really tell you not to eat fruit from any tree in the garden?'[13]

Unable to take her eyes off the creature, she replies, 'We may eat the fruit of any tree in the garden, except the tree in the middle of it. God told us not to eat the fruit of that tree or even touch it; if we do, we will die.'[14]

'I feel like running out there and stopping her from listening to that monster!' cries Natasha.

Mr Coles looks at her thoughtfully. 'I think we all feel like doing that, seeing as we know what happens next. If we were in Eve's place, I'm sure most of us would have done the same.'

'I wouldn't,' says Alan, 'because I don't like fruit.'

'Trust you to come out with a stupid comment like that,' says Natasha, unimpressed by his sense of humour. 'You may not have been tempted to take the fruit, but you wouldn't have got through the first day in this beautiful place without sinning!'

'That's enough, you two,' interrupts Mr Coles. 'Now is really not the moment.'

They all focus again on the scene in front of them. The snake moves closer to Eve, its face now only inches away from hers. Again, in that most evil of voices, they hear it speak: 'That's not true; you will not die. God said that, because he knows that when you eat it you will be like God and know what is good and what is bad.'[15]

At that moment, Eve averts her eyes from the snake's, and gazes up into the tree. You can tell from the eager expression on her face that she loves what she sees. The fruit just looks so good! She stretches up and plucks a huge juicy piece, and then bites into it. The watching class can almost feel what she is experiencing. The fruit is obviously so good to eat.

As Eve bites into the fruit, the snake watches her, and the others can just catch the sound of faint, mocking laughter. It is a nasty sound, and leaves them all feeling a little edgy.

Eve then turns and calls to Adam. He appears from behind one of the trees, about 20 metres away, and runs over to join Eve. She holds out some of the delicious fruit to him. He takes it and opens his mouth. At the exact moment that he takes a bite, a cold wind sweeps across the garden. Mr Coles and the group sense that something quite awful has happened. The snake crawls away. Evil has triumphed.

'I don't know why, but I feel scared,' says Sarah.

'I know what you mean,' agrees Bronagh. 'Just a moment ago, it was so wonderful to be here, but now there's some kind of evil presence in the air.'

Adam and Eve suddenly dart behind the nearest tree. It is a giant fig tree, and the leaves are huge. They both strip some of the leaves from the tree, manage to tie them together, and then use the leaves to cover themselves. It's no longer peaceful and idyllic: everything has changed. Adam and Eve are clearly very embarrassed about being naked.

'Do they now know what is good and what is evil, sir?' Natasha asks Mr Coles.

'Yes, they do,' replies Mr Coles.

'But didn't they know that already, sir, before they ate the fruit?' asks John.

Before Mr Coles can respond, Bronagh steps in and says, 'Maybe they always knew the difference between good and evil, in some way. It would probably be quite difficult to know fully, as they hadn't experienced evil yet. But that snake, or Satan, or whatever you want to call him, has obviously offered them something more, a God-like knowledge of good and evil.'

'I think that's very well put, Bronagh. Well done!' says Mr Coles.

As they watch Adam and Eve in their desperate attempt to cover their nakedness, the whole group just feel pity. Because of what has happened, Adam and Eve must be feeling ashamed, and no longer able to face God.

Doyin looks at the others, with tears in her eyes. 'They have gained some sort of knowledge, you know, and I think that knowledge is all about what they have both now lost—that special relationship they had with God.'

Natasha walks over and comforts Doyin with a hug.

Everyone else stands there in silence. What else can anyone say?

Adam and Eve's desperate attempt to cover themselves is clearly not just about covering their sexual organs. It is as if they are trying to cover the whole of themselves. They seem to want to hide from

God totally. They can no longer face him. That closeness is what they have now lost.

Steven says softly, 'It's almost pathetic to see, sir. A minute ago, they were like the king and queen of the world, and now look at them.'

'This is what happens when we disobey God,' says Shaheda.

'Sir, in my church I think I was taught once that Adam and Eve didn't cover themselves because they were physically naked, but because they were spiritually naked,' says Natasha after another pause.

'I think you're right,' replies Mr Coles, flicking through his Bible. He reads aloud a passage that he has found.

There is nothing that can be hidden from God; everything in all creation is exposed and lies open before his eyes. And it is to him that we must all give an account of ourselves.[16]

'This passage from Hebrews is pretty much what you're talking about, Natasha.'

'Sir, whose fault was it, then?' asks Jilani. 'Was it Adam's fault or Eve's fault, because she took the fruit?'

'That's a very good question.'

'You be careful what you say now, sir!' jokes Bronagh. 'Don't go blaming everything on women!'

'All I can do is to let you know what other people have said about this incident,' replies Mr Coles. 'Some have blamed it totally on the woman. We've seen that it was the woman who was tempted, and she did take the forbidden fruit. Some people say it was even worse—that she got Adam to eat the fruit as well, getting him into trouble.'

'Definitely the woman's fault, I reckon,' says Alan, nodding his head as if that's the end of the matter. Natasha gives Alan a playful slap around the head, and tells him to shut up.

'As I was saying,' continues Mr Coles, 'even Paul in his first letter to Timothy wrote, "And it was not Adam who was deceived; it was the woman who was deceived and broke God's law."[17] There are those who believe that it was Eve who got the whole human race into trouble. They argue that it was Adam's so-called companion who led to our downfall.'

'Well, I think that's complete rubbish,' shouts Sarah. 'If anything, it's men that always cause the trouble!'

'Yeah, you go girl!' the other girls cheer her on.

'Well, I'll now explain to you what others teach—those who believe that ultimately it was Adam's fault,' says Mr Coles, calming them all down. 'I'd like you to get back on the bus now, as we need to move forward in time a couple of hours. We need to be here in the early evening, when the next part of the story will unfold.'

They all climb back on board. Mr Coles asks everyone to be quiet so that he can carry on talking about what has happened. 'Right, let me just explain why many Christians think it was Adam who brought sin into the world.'

'Yes, you tell us,' shouts Sarah. 'Tell us how it was the man who brought sin into the world!'

Mr Coles continues. 'It was Adam who was told that he could not eat any fruit from the tree of knowledge of good and evil—'

'But it was the woman who took the fruit and got the man into trouble,' interrupts Alan.

'Yes, Alan,' replies Mr Coles. 'Eve may have been the one who took the fruit from the tree, having been tempted by the snake, but it was Adam who brought sin into the world. It is Adam who is the head of the whole human race. It was to him that the commandment was given. He was responsible for Eve. In Paul's letter to the Romans, chapter 5 verse 12, it says, "Sin came into the world through one man, and his sin brought death with it. As a result, death has spread to the whole human race because everyone has sinned."'

'I reckon the fairest thing to say, sir, is that both the man and the woman were equally responsible for sin coming into the world,' says Bronagh.

'I can agree with that,' adds Boris.

John says, 'In a way, that's what Paul thinks. One minute he writes that it was the "woman who was deceived" and then he writes that sin came into the world "through one man".'

Mr Coles finishes by saying that it would be best if they all agreed that it was the man and the woman who were equally responsible for bringing sin into the world. The whole class nod in agreement.

Mr Coles then programmes the time machine to take them forward in time by a few hours. Within a couple of seconds, they find themselves still in the same day, but now it is early evening. Once again they get out of the bus.

Chapter 10

God's judgment

Once they are all out, the class notice Adam and Eve walking in the garden a few hundred metres in front of them. Then they suddenly hear a strong wind blowing in one of the magnificent trees close by. No sooner have Adam and Eve heard the blowing wind than they run away and hide behind another tree. As Mr Coles and the pupils stand there watching, they hear a voice booming from the wind blowing in the tree.

'Where are you?' It is God who is speaking.

'There's something different about the way God sounds now, don't you think?' says John, nervously.

'John's right,' whispers Bronagh.

'I think what we can hear now is a vengeful God,' says Mr Coles, sadly.

'I suppose that's what happens when you upset him,' whispers Natasha.

As soon as God has asked where Adam and Eve are, Adam's head appears from behind the tree and he answers God: 'I heard you in the garden; I was afraid and hid from you, because I was naked.'[18]

God replies, asking how they have become aware of their nakedness, and whether they have eaten from the forbidden tree. Adam responds with a touch of defiance: 'The woman you put here with me gave me the fruit, and I ate it.' God's voice asks the woman why she has done this, and she replies, 'The snake tricked me into eating it.'[19]

'That's quite hilarious,' says Alan to Mr Coles.

'What are you talking about, Alan?' says Natasha.

'The way they blame someone else for having done wrong. Adam blames Eve, and Eve blames the snake! At least I always own up, sir, when I've got into trouble.'

Bronagh says, 'It's typical of people, though; once you've done something wrong, it's easy to blame it on someone else. We've all done that. It seems as if blaming other people has been going on from the very beginning.'

'A very good point,' Mr Coles answers.

'It's so difficult to know who was really at fault here,' says Boris thoughtfully. 'I'm surprised that Adam didn't blame God; he was the one who created Eve as a companion for Adam.'

'I was thinking the same,' adds John. 'Also, if the snake really does represent Satan, then we can't ignore how powerful Satan is. If it was one of us who was Adam or Eve, we would have probably been tempted just as much.'

They all fall silent again as the voice of God fills the air around them, speaking to the snake.

You will be punished for this; you alone of all the animals must bear this curse: from now on you must crawl on your belly, and you will have to eat dust as long as you live. I will make you and the woman hate each other; her offspring and yours will always be enemies. Her offspring will crush your head, and you will bite her offspring's heel.[20]

'What on earth was all that about?' asks Alan, looking totally bemused.

'I know, I know!' shouts Natasha.

'Go on then, Natasha,' nods Mr Coles. 'Please tell us.'

'In church, a few months ago, our pastor told us all about this story. He pointed out that God doesn't question the snake, and that's because God is well aware that the snake is not really to blame for what happened. One day there will be someone who comes and takes the blame. The sentence on the snake is really addressed to the one who is going to come.'

'Who are you talking about?' asks Sarah.

'She's talking about Jesus,' answers Doyin. 'He's the one who will come and take the blame.'

'So what's all this crawling and eating dust about?' asks Jilani.

Natasha continues. 'The snake was once an animal that moved gracefully on the ground. Now it is an animal that crawls on its belly. "Eating dust" is a sign of being defeated. Our pastor told us that in the book of Micah, somewhere it says…' (she breaks off and leafs through the pages). 'Here it is! "They will crawl in the dust like snakes; they will come from their fortresses, trembling and afraid. They will turn in fear to the Lord our God."' [21]

'Well done,' says Mr Coles enthusiastically. 'From now on the snake will be humbled and defeated. Snakes will always be attacked from now on, whenever people see one.'

'They'll also attack back!' shouts Jilani. 'I hate snakes!'

'Jilani is right,' continues Mr Coles. 'People will still always come out on top in this struggle, though. Just as the snake creeps up on its prey, so the unseen enemy will also attack human beings. But, with the help of God, people will be able to fight this unseen enemy, and win. The enemy will be humiliated and made to eat the dust from the ground.'

'Are you talking about Satan being the unseen enemy?' asks Bronagh.

'Exactly!' answers Mr Coles.

'It's a very clever symbol, using the snake to mean sin and temptation,' adds John. 'Whenever we see a snake now, it will remind us of how sin can creep up and attack us suddenly. I suppose people must take care to keep a look-out for sin, just as we have to keep a look-out for snakes—though not in London, of course!'

'Nice one, Professor John!' laughs Jilani.

'Nice one, definitely,' adds Mr Coles. 'You really have grasped the meaning of this story.'

'I think it's sad being here now,' says Shaheda. 'Not long ago, we were sitting in paradise, and it was so wonderful. Now it feels ordinary. I might as well be back in school or back home.'

'I know what you mean,' responds Bronagh. 'Now that sin has come into the world, that heavenly feeling I had inside me has gone.'

'I've never really believed in anything, as you all know,' says Alan. 'But there was something so wonderful about this place before sin came into the world. I want to feel it again.'

'Do you believe in God now?' asks Jilani.

'How can I not believe in God, having seen all this?' says Alan.

Mr Coles waves his hand to quieten them down. 'Just as people will now have a constant battle with snakes, people will now have a constant battle with evil. This evil is going to be everywhere and will always try to "snap at our heels".'

'Does that mean we should wear thick boots then?'

They all laugh. Jilani, the class clown, strikes again!

'To protect against snakes, maybe,' laughs Mr Coles. 'Since this moment in time, which we have all witnessed, there has been a continual battle against evil. But it is a battle that people will win in the end. I think that's what God meant when he said that he would "crush the head" of the snake.'

'Is it Jesus who finally "crushes the head"?' asks Boris.

'That's what I was told in church,' answers Natasha.

'It is Jesus. Well done,' acknowledges Mr Coles. 'Since this moment in time, there has been a continual battle between people and snakes, and between the hidden enemy and people. This is how things were until God came to us as a man. The snake will be defeated by the ultimate man.'

'Sounds a bit like Superman coming to the rescue,' laughs Steven.

'That's not a bad way to describe it,' Mr Coles agrees, with a smile.

'As a Muslim,' adds Jilani, 'I don't believe that Jesus is God's Son, but in a way there was something quite "super" about him as a prophet.'

'That's right,' says Shaheda. 'We believe in the virgin birth, and we believe that Jesus was a miracle worker.'

'Thanks, you two,' says Mr Coles, delighted. 'It's always wonderful when any of you share your own beliefs with the class, and I always appreciate how you listen to and respect each other's views.'

Mr Coles then asks them all to be quiet and listen to what God is saying to the woman: 'I will increase your trouble in pregnancy and your pain in giving birth. In spite of this, you will still have desire for your husband, yet you will be subject to him.'[22]

'That's not fair,' shouts Bronagh. 'First, the woman is now going to have pain being pregnant—backaches, morning sickness and all the rest of it—and then she'll be in pain giving birth!'

'And then she has to be "subject to her husband",' adds Sarah. 'What's all that about then?'

'Could I answer that, please, sir?' Steven breaks in.

'Here we go,' says Bronagh. 'All the men are going to gang up against us now!'

'Don't be silly, folks,' says Mr Coles. 'Let's see what Steven has to say about it.'

All eyes are on Steven.

'All I want to say is what I learned in church about this story,' Steven begins. 'By the way, my minister at church is a woman, and it was her who taught me all about this story in Genesis. She said that everything was perfect in the beginning—which is what we've all seen. And what God planned in the beginning was that producing children would be a duty and a blessing. But now that sin has entered the world, this blessing will involve serious pain. But people can still enjoy sex to make children, and that's because God has mercy on us.'

Bronagh adds, 'There seems to be no real way for a woman to avoid this punishment. She'll always want her husband, but he'll be able to dominate her. Once, they were both equal, but now the woman has lost her status.'

Mr Coles nods at Bronagh. 'Many Bible scholars teach that although in Genesis the writers simply talk about the pain of childbirth, the real definition of the word "pain" means the general pain and misery of life. Let's listen to what God has to say to Adam now.'

'Do we have to?' asks Alan. 'I'm getting fed up with all this talk of sin and misery.'

'Well,' chuckles Natasha, 'you're going to have to get used to it. Sin has entered the world, and there's going to be a lot of misery from now on.'

'God help us,' sighs Alan.

'A good point,' laughs Natasha. 'God will help us! Sin has entered the world, but God will help us. That is the hope that we can have.'

'I hope so,' says Alan. 'I need a bit of hope after all this depressing stuff in the garden of Eden.'

'I know it's not pleasant to be here, witnessing sin and evil entering the world,' says Mr Coles. 'But we should listen to what God says to Adam.'

God's voice booms out.

You listened to your wife and ate the fruit which I told you not to eat. Because of what you have done, the ground will be under a curse. You will have to work hard all your life to make it produce enough food for you. It will produce weeds and thorns, and you will have to eat wild plants. You will have to work hard and sweat to make the soil produce anything, until you go back to the soil from which you were formed. You were made from soil, and you will become soil again.'[23]

'It's quite strange that the man doesn't get cursed like the snake was cursed. I suppose that's because the man is on his own, and there is nothing else that can be cursed,' comments Steven.

'What on earth are you talking about?' asks Sarah.

'What I'm saying is that the snake is cursed because it represents the evil behind it—Satan. The ground is cursed, because it represents the man. But the man is on his own.'

'That makes more sense,' says Sarah.

John adds, 'That's why we have to work so hard to provide food.

In Paradise there was beautiful food everywhere, but now it will always be a struggle to find enough. As well as having to deal with all the thorns and thistles, which didn't exist in Eden, we'll have to deal with being sinners.'

Mr Coles looks round the group. 'Things could have been a lot worse. I think that God has been quite merciful.'

'I think that too,' Bronagh agrees. 'It was Satan who caused the man and woman to sin. I think God has already planned that one day this whole situation will be reversed.'

'Amen to that!' cheers Natasha.

They all turn towards Adam and Eve. They see Adam walk up to Eve. He puts a comforting arm round her shoulder and says to her, 'Your name will now be Eve, because you will be the mother of all human beings.'[24]

Mr Coles tells the class that by renaming her, Adam is exerting his new authority: 'He's now the boss.'

What happens next is quite strange to see. As they watch Adam and Eve, they see some clothing appear mysteriously from the tree where God has been speaking. The clothing is made out of animal skins. Although Adam and Eve have never worn clothes before, they seem to know exactly what to do, as they both know that they are naked and want to cover themselves.

'It's about time that they put some clothes on!' says Jilani to Mr Coles. 'Sir, those are animal skins they're wearing. Does that mean some animals have been killed?'

'That's a really good question,' agrees John.

'Well, I'm not stupid all the time, you know!'

'That is a good point,' says Mr Coles. 'There has been no death at all up to this point. Because people have now sinned, death has come into the world.'

'You mean some animals had to die just so that Adam and Eve can stand in front of God without feeling embarrassed,' says Bronagh rather sadly.

Natasha looks up, eyes wide, as if she has just been enlightened. 'In a way, that's like the first ever sacrifice made so that people can face God. One day there will be the last sacrifice made, and that will be the most important of all.'

Jilani butts in, 'I know what you're going to say. You believe as a Christian that Jesus was the last sacrifice.'

'Exactly!' Natasha says emphatically.

'Wow! That really was a moment of inspiration, Natasha,' says Mr Coles.

As they stand there, contemplating Natasha's divine inspiration, they hear the voice of God once again. 'Now the man has become like one of us and has knowledge of what is good and what is bad. He must not be allowed to take fruit from the tree that gives life, eat it, and live for ever.'[25]

All of a sudden, a terrible wind blows from the tree, and lightning starts to flash from the skies. Adam and Eve look terrified, and they turn and start to run away from the garden. They have been thrown out of Paradise.

Mr Coles tells the class that they will be leaving soon. Before they can move, they see something quite terrifying. No wonder Adam and Eve ran away! Some strange 'beings' have appeared in the garden. They are the cherubim, God's guardian angels. Sadly, these heavenly beings are to be a barrier between God and human beings. The powerful storm that is raging all around them is meant to exclude human beings from this wonderful garden, the place of beauty and peace.

A couple of the pupils have tears in their eyes. To have seen Paradise, and then to witness sin coming into the world, has been awful. Nothing could be worse than having to leave Eden. They remain in silence for a moment, gathering their thoughts, reflecting on how this experience will influence them for the rest of their lives.

Mr Coles then leads them back to the time machine. He explains that they will travel forward in time approximately 18 years from now.

'Why 18 years, sir?' several of the pupils ask at once.

Mr Coles answers, 'The Bible tells us that after Adam and Eve were thrown out of the garden, they had intercourse, and gave birth to Cain. Later, they give birth to Abel. When the children were older, Cain became a farmer and Abel became a shepherd. So, folks, sit tight, and here we go. Should take only a few seconds.'

'I love this time machine!' says Alan.

It's murder!

When the short journey is over, everyone looks out of the minibus window.

'Who are all those people?' asks Doyin.

'That's Adam and Eve over there,' Mr Coles points, 'and the other people are their sons and daughters.'

'Wow!' says Natasha. 'What a huge family.'

Alan then asks, 'Sir, we know that Adam and Eve were married and had all these children that we can see here, but who will they marry? They're brothers and sisters, so they obviously can't marry each other.'

'That's a really good point,' adds Jilani.

'It's a brilliant point,' says Mr Coles. 'We'll deal with that question a little later, when we see what happens.'

'That's really got me thinking,' says Bronagh. 'Nice one, Alan!'

'Anyway, let's focus on what's about to happen here today,' says Mr Coles.

'And what is about to happen here today, sir?' asks Alan. 'Something a little more cheerful than what we've just seen, I hope!'

'Actually, Alan, we are about to witness a murder,' says Mr Coles.

'Blimey!' exclaims Alan. 'Things are going from bad to worse!'

'I'd like everyone to get out of the bus now,' orders Mr Coles. They all disembark.

Mr Coles indicates a field a short distance away. 'Look over there, please,' he says. 'The man you can see working in the field is Cain. He's a farmer.'

'Oh my Lord!' shouts Natasha. 'We're about to witness Cain killing his brother!'

'All because Adam and Eve ate the fruit,' sighs Doyin. 'Now the world's really in a mess.'

Mr Coles tells them that Natasha is correct. He adds that they won't be seeing the actual murder, but they will watch what happens just before, and the events that occur afterwards.

'So we're not watching the murder, then?' asks Alan.

'Don't be so sick!' Bronagh frowns at him.

Mr Coles quietens them down, and asks them to watch carefully what is about to happen.

They all look over at Cain in the field. He is harvesting with a sickle. After a few moments, he collects up some of his harvest and places it on the ground. He then looks up, and seems to be offering some kind of a prayer of thanksgiving. He is dedicating the harvest to God.

A little later, they see Abel arrive. On his shoulders he is carrying a young lamb. He walks over to where Cain has just left his offering. With a sharp knife, he slits the animal's throat, killing it instantly. Some of the pupils turn their heads, feeling a little queasy. Abel also offers a prayer of thanksgiving, and holds up the best parts of the lamb in dedication to God.

Mr Coles and the rest of the group suddenly hear God speak again, in their own langauages. They hear God thanking Abel for his wonderful offering. They also hear God totally rejecting Cain's offering. Cain's face is furrowed with anger. He shakes his fist and stamps around furiously. They then hear God speak again: 'Why are you angry? Why that scowl on your face? If you had done the right thing, you would be smiling; but because you have done evil, sin is crouching at your door. It wants to rule you, but you must overcome it.'[26]

Steven turns to Mr Coles. 'That seems a bit harsh. What on earth did Cain do wrong?'

'It seemed like a nice offering to me,' says Boris.

'Why is God so angry with Cain, sir?' asks Sarah. 'I thought his offering was a good one—better than all that blood and mess!'

'These are good questions,' Mr Coles responds. 'Let's take a look in the Bible to find some answers.' He turns to Genesis chapter 4.

'It's quite clear in the biblical account that Cain's offering is not really anything special. It just says that Cain offered 'some of his harvest'. But Abel offered the firstborn lamb, and gave the Lord the best parts of that lamb. I think that Cain didn't really put much effort into his offering. It didn't come from the heart.'

'I know what you're saying, sir,' says Sarah. 'But it still seems a bit mean of God to reject Cain's offering.'

Bronagh turns to Sarah and asks, 'If someone gave you a present for your birthday, and then you found out that this person really hated you, and they only gave you a present because they felt they had to, how would you feel?'

'OK,' says Sarah. 'I get your point. If Cain's attitude is the same, and God knows it, perhaps he does have the right to be angry and reject the offering.'

'I would imagine that Cain has had this problem for quite a while,' Mr Coles continues. 'Look how furious he is! I think he may have been jealous for a long time. He looks in a terrible state.'

After a while, Cain seems to calm down. He walks over to Abel and seems to be telling his brother that he is sorry. Then he puts a hand on his brother's arm and pulls him off towards one of the fields. They carry on walking until Mr Coles and his group can barely see them. They can't follow, as they have to stay inside the safety beam. As Cain and Abel continue walking along, side by side, they see Cain bend down and pick up some sort of object, perhaps a large stone. Although the two brothers are far away now, the group can just see Cain smashing this object down on Abel's head. Abel immediately falls to the ground.

'I'm glad that was in the distance, sir,' says Shaheda.

'Me too,' says Bronagh with a shudder. 'It's quite strange witnessing this murder. I hear about it quite often, being a Christian. In a funny way, though, I actually wasn't very shocked. We knew it was going to happen.'

'Shame we weren't a bit closer,' says Steven.

'Don't be so sick,' says Doyin.

Mr Coles says, 'We have just witnessed the first murder on this planet. It seems that Adam and Eve's meal from the forbidden tree has now begun producing some very bitter fruit indeed.'

They stand in silence for a while, pondering on what Mr Coles has said.

'Do you mean like gooseberries?' asks Jilani.

'You silly clown!' shouts Bronagh. 'What Mr Coles just said was really important, and you have to spoil it.'

'No, no,' says Mr Coles. 'It's good to have Jilani along. We've seen something quite awful, and yet Jilani is able to make us laugh.'

They all look up to see Cain walking back towards them.

'OK,' says Mr Coles. 'Would someone like to volunteer to read part of Genesis chapter four? I'd like us to discover what God now says to Cain.'

Boris puts his hand up to volunteer.

'Let's turn to Genesis chapter 4, verses 9 to 15,' Mr Coles goes on. 'Boris, could you begin, please.'

Boris reads:

The Lord asked Cain, 'Where is your brother Abel?'

He answered, 'I don't know. Am I supposed to take care of my brother?'

Then the Lord said, 'Why have you done this terrible thing? Your brother's blood is crying out to me from the ground, like a voice calling for revenge. You are placed under a curse and can no longer farm the soil. It has soaked up your brother's blood as if it had opened up its mouth to receive it when you killed him. If you try to grow crops, the soil will not produce anything; you will be a homeless wanderer on the earth.'

And Cain said to the Lord, 'This punishment is too hard for me to bear. You are driving me off the land and away from your presence. I will be a homeless wanderer on the earth, and anyone who finds me will kill me.'

But the Lord answered, 'No. If anyone kills you, seven lives will be taken in revenge.'

As Cain comes closer to the group, they notice that his face has become distorted, discoloured and almost diseased-looking. One or two of the pupils turn away, unable to bear the sight.

'What on earth is happening to his face?' asks Boris.

Mr Coles answers, 'The Bible tells us that God put a mark on Cain so that anyone who met him would not kill him.'

'No one is going to go near him with a face like that,' says Steven.

'It's the same reason why none of us go near you, Steven,' teases Doyin.

The others all laugh.

'Seriously, though,' says Mr Coles, 'it does look quite repulsive. But it will stop anyone from killing him.'

'Cain didn't seem very sorry for what he had done, did he, sir?' asks Boris.

'That's true,' answers Mr Coles. 'I remember that Adam went to hide after his sin, but Cain actually argues with God. We would all think that we should look after our own brothers, but not Cain. So he is told to live the rest of his life in the desert, where it will be a continual struggle to stay alive, looking for food and water.'

'I can't believe that he didn't say sorry to God,' says Bronagh. 'He's only thinking about himself. The only thing that seems to bother him is that he has lost the blessings God had given him. He's no longer a farmer; he no longer has God to protect him. That's pretty awful!'

'You're totally correct,' says Mr Coles. 'All he's worried about is what the future has in store for him.'

They watch Cain. He looks over his fields once more, and then heads off east.

Mr Coles tells the group that it's time to get back into the bus.

John asks whether they could have another drink. Mr Coles takes out some mineral water, Coke and lemonade, and the pupils help themselves.

Once their thirst is quenched, Mr Coles asks for silence. 'Listen— a while ago, Alan asked a really good question.'

'That's right!' shouts out Bronagh. 'After Adam and Eve, who married who?'

Mr Coles continues. 'This is a really fascinating point. In Genesis chapter 4, verse 17, we read that Cain had a wife. The big question, therefore, is where did Cain get his wife?

Chapter 12

Who married whom?

'This is a really tricky situation,' says Natasha.

'In what way?' asks Mr Coles.

'Well, we've seen that there was only one man in the beginning, and that was Adam, made out of dust. That would mean, sir, that Cain's wife must be a descendant of Adam.'

'That's right,' says John. 'We haven't seen any other people around, except for Adam's descendants. Adam and Eve are quite simply the father and mother of everyone.'

Doyin adds, 'In the book of Acts, it does say, "From one human being he created all races on earth and made them live throughout the whole earth."' [27]

'Let's get to the main point, though, shall we?' asks Alan. 'The simple question is, did brothers and sisters have to marry each other in the beginning?'

Mr Coles turns towards Alan. 'The simple answer, Alan, is: yes, they must have.'

'But that's awful!' shouts Bronagh.

'To us, now, it may seem awful, and, yes, it's against the law. But back then, it was clearly not an issue. The idea of marrying a close relative seems quite absurd to us, but here, at the beginning, we are all relations.'

'I think I get your drift, sir,' says Natasha.

Bronagh is also beginning to understand. 'Yes, it's just dawned on me—all wives and husbands are related to each other, even before they meet. And the simple reason is that everyone is descended from Adam and Eve.'

John then asks, 'But in the Old Testament somewhere, I'm sure

Moses stopped close relatives from marrying.'

'John is correct,' says Mr Coles. 'In the book of Leviticus, chapter 18, there is a whole list of people whom you couldn't have intercourse with, including sisters, stepsisters, aunts, and so on. The main thing to bear in mind, though, is that these laws came at the time of Moses, so presumably, before that time, brothers and sisters—or stepsisters—could marry. The only requirement about marriage in Genesis seems to be that a man has to marry a woman, and that the partnership is for life. In Genesis chapter 20, verse 12, Abraham says about Sarah, "She really is my sister. She is the daughter of my father, but not of my mother, and I married her." This marriage was even blessed by God. It was much, much later that Moses came along and gave laws that forbade these marriages.'

'I can hear what you're saying, sir,' says Jilani, looking a little confused. 'But I always thought that if a brother and sister had sex together, and she got pregnant, wouldn't the child end up being a bit of a loony with an ugly face?'

'You have such a way with words,' says Doyin, giggling.

'He is daft,' laughs Bronagh. 'But he does have a really good point. Wasn't the royal family a bit mad centuries ago because of intermarrying? What about that film, *Deliverance*, where they come across a group of deformed people? They were all inbred.'

'That's a wicked film,' says Alan. 'That's what Jilani meant about being loony and ugly. That's how they all looked in that film.'

'What you're all chatting about is quite true,' replies Mr Coles. 'Today, if brothers and sisters have children, it's very likely that they will be deformed in some way. The reason is all to do with genetics, which I'm afraid I know very little about.'

Boris puts his hand up and asks if he can try to explain the genetic problem. 'Be my guest,' says Mr Coles.

'When a couple are married and have children,' Boris begins, 'the children inherit good genes and bad genes. The bad genes, containing mistakes, will be different depending on whether they come from the mum or the dad, and usually the good genes override the bad genes so that the bad ones can't do any harm. The problem with a brother and sister marrying is that they both have the same bad genes, because of inheriting them from the same parents. So *their* children can get both bad genes, which won't be overridden by a good gene. The bad genes together will result in the child being born seriously deformed in some way, depending on which genes were bad.'[28]

'Wow!' shouts Alan, looking really impressed. 'Now who's the professor?'

Mr Coles grins at Boris. 'Well done! You explained that really well. You should become a teacher, you know.'

'I have been thinking about it, sir.'

'You must be mad!' laughs Jilani. 'Having to deal with a load of loonies like us every day!'

Shaheda puts up her hand.

'What is it?' asks Mr Coles.

'Boris has explained how all this gene business works. That's fair enough. But how does it explain brothers and sisters being able to marry here, and the children having no defects?'

'I can't answer that one, I'm afraid,' says Boris.

Mr Coles regains their attention and says, 'I imagine that the answer is quite simple. Based on what Boris has said, it would seem that these bad genes continue from generation to generation. But Adam and Eve are the first two people on earth. They won't have any bad genes. They are perfect. Therefore their sons and daughters will have inherited pretty much perfect genes.'

'Why do you say "pretty much perfect", sir?' asks Bronagh.

'I say that because sin and evil have now entered the world, and, slowly but surely, genes will start becoming defective.'

'So, at the moment, brothers and sisters will be able to marry and produce children,' says Alan.

'So what seemed like a big mystery now makes perfect sense,' exclaims Natasha. 'Obviously, by the time of Moses there were quite a few genetic defects floating around, and that explains why Moses had to give the rules about who you could and couldn't marry.'

'This is all really amazing,' says John thoughtfully. 'We've travelled back to the very beginning, but of course we're looking at things with 21st-century minds, like this question about brothers and sisters.'

'I reckon we should all remember that as we continue our journey through time,' says Mr Coles.

'Are we going to travel through the whole book of Genesis?' asks Jilani.

'We won't have time, I'm afraid,' answers Mr Coles.

'Don't we have all the time in the world?' asks Sarah. 'Surely we can stay here for as long as we want, and just return two or three hours after we left.'

Jilani adds, 'We could stay here for the next 50 years, couldn't we, and still get back to school a few hours after we left?'

'Let's not get into this time travel theory again, please,' pleads Mr Coles. 'We've been here for a couple of hours now, and we'll spend maybe three hours more, before we travel back.'

'I can't believe it!' Sarah shakes her head. 'We've only been here for a couple of hours, and we've seen the whole world created, dinosaurs, naked people running around, Satan tempting Adam and Eve, and the first murder, all in two hours!'

'Try telling our parents that when we get home,' laughs Bronagh, 'and they'll be sending us to a psychiatrist. Anyway, sir, where are we off to next?'

'A good question,' says Mr Coles. 'I think I'm going to set the dial to take us to the time of Noah.'

'Yeah!' shouts Jilani. 'He's also one of our prophets in Islam. Now we'll see a wicked flood.'

'Not more water,' moans Alan. 'On day one we were on a raging ocean, and now we're going to another one.'

'Stop complaining,' retorts Doyin. 'This should be excellent.'

'It might be excellent,' says Mr Coles, 'but the flood happened for a reason. It happened because humankind became so evil that God destroyed them all, except for Noah and his family. Let's get ready to move forward in time, and find out what really happened. And before we move, let's turn to Genesis chapter 6.'

The animals go in
two by two

Mr Coles asks Sarah to read Genesis chapter 6, verses 5 to 8. Sarah clears her throat and reads:

When the Lord saw how wicked everyone on earth was and how evil their thoughts were all the time, he was sorry that he had ever made them and put them on the earth. He was so filled with regret that he said, 'I will wipe out these people I have created, and also the animals and the birds, because I am sorry that I made any of them.' But the Lord was pleased with Noah.

'Thank you, Sarah,' says Mr Coles. 'That was beautifully read.'

'How terrible is that?' says Alan. 'God creates a beautiful world, and before we know it, humans have to go and ruin everything.'

Mr Coles tells them that they are about to move forward in time. They all buckle themselves in. Mr Coles goes on, 'What Alan says is correct. It is a terrible thing. Before we get to the time of Noah, we'll just observe what is happening with humankind, and see what's gone wrong.'

He moves a few dials on the time machine. Light seems to flicker outside the bus, and all goes a little blurred for a few moments. When the minibus comes to rest, they are shocked at what they can see through the windows. For a start, there are thousands of people scattered everywhere, and tents all over the place. It is quite a change from the tranquillity of the beautiful garden of Eden.

'How many people do you reckon there are on the earth now, sir?' asks Shaheda.

'I've heard some Christians say that there could have been at least a billion people alive by now,' says Mr Coles.

'Blimey, sir, that many?' asks Sarah.

'That's what I've heard.'

Steven suddenly points out of the window, shouting, 'Look what's happening over there!'

They all look in the direction he is pointing, and see a vicious fight going on, involving seven or eight men. One man is being beaten over the head with a large stone. He falls to the ground and lies motionless. A woman runs over and kneels beside him, screaming. There is blood everywhere. No one comes to help her or the man. From what the onlookers in the minibus can see, the man is dead.

Alan says slowly, 'Violence in a film is one thing, but to see all this is just sickening.'

A hundred metres away to the left, they glimpse three men, clearly drunk, chasing a terrified woman. Other men are standing by, watching and laughing. Bronagh asks Mr Coles if they can move on. 'Even the East End on a Friday night isn't as bad as this,' she says.

'The East End is Paradise compared to that,' says Alan grimly.

Mr Coles says, 'If there are a billion people on the planet by now, they are all guilty of behaving like this, because the Lord is soon going to destroy the lot.'

'Judging by what we just saw,' says Natasha, 'I don't think anybody in the world knows what it means to be good, or how to love and worship God. Are you sure your time machine didn't travel to hell instead?'

'That's a pretty good description of what is going on out there,' says Mr Coles.

'Can we move on and find the few good people that still exist, out of the billion that are here?' asks Boris.

'The minibus is in the right time zone, but I'll just need to adjust its position to take us to Noah and his family,' Mr Coles says. 'It'll only take a second.'

A moment later, Mr Coles tells them to look out of the windows on the left of the minibus. There they see a man with his arms raised to the sky in prayer. Behind him is a crowd of others—young and old, men, women and children—also praying.

'This must be good old Noah!' shouts Jilani. 'He's one of our prophets. We call him Nuh.'

'It sounds like Noah,' nods Doyin.

'This lot are totally different from the others we saw,' says Alan.

'You can even see in their faces that they're good people,' says Natasha. 'It's hard to believe that out of a billion people, if that's how many are now on the earth, there's only Noah and his wife and their children's families who are good.'

As they are watching, they see Noah suddenly look round. At this point, all on board the bus once again hear the voice of God:

Noah, I have decided to put an end to the whole human race. I will destroy them completely, because the world is full of their violent deeds. Build a boat for yourself out of good timber; make rooms in it and cover it with tar inside and out. Make it 133 metres long, 22 metres wide, and 13 metres high. Make a roof for the boat and leave a space of 44 centimetres between the roof and the sides. Build it with three decks and put a door in the side. I am going to send a flood on the earth to destroy every living being. Everything on the earth will die, but I will make a covenant with you. Go into the boat with your wife, your sons, and their wives. Take into the boat with you a male and a female of every kind of animal and of every kind of bird, in order to keep them alive. Take along all kinds of food for you and for them.' [29]

'Wow!' says Doyin. 'This is the story of Noah's ark. It's been my favourite ever since I heard it in Sunday school when I was little. We used to sing loads of songs about Noah and his ark.'

'Don't start singing any now, though,' laughs Sarah, 'You've got a terrible voice!'

'Yeah,' adds Jilani, 'you might scare off the animals!'

Mr Coles motions with his hand to get them quiet. 'Let's step out of the bus, please, so that we can see what happens when Noah tells his family about the boat.' As they emerge, the class find that once again they can understand what is being said.

Noah is calling his family to gather round. 'My dear children. The Lord has just spoken to me, and he has told me a terrible thing. He has looked down upon the world and has seen how evil his people have become. He is sorry that he ever created them. God is going to punish them all with a mighty flood. But he has looked upon our family kindly, and we will not be destroyed with the rest of humanity. We are to build a huge boat. We will be spared, and two of every type of animal will also be spared.'

Noah's three sons, Shem, Ham and Japheth, push forward to their father's side, looking very concerned.

'Is this really true, father?' asks Shem. 'How are we going to build this boat? Are you sure that's what God said to you? Where is all the water going to come from?'

'So many questions, my son,' replies Noah, calmly. 'All my life I have taught you to trust in the Lord, and God has blessed us for it. He has now given us this new command. It is a terrible thing, I know, but we have seen how evil the people are. We are taunted every day because of our steadfast faith in the Lord. Keep your faith now, my sons, more than ever. God has spoken, and we are to obey.'

Noah hugs his three sons, and they seem to accept that Noah has spoken truthfully. They question him no more.

Bronagh says quite emotionally, 'That is real faith, sir. How many of us would have accepted something like that? This has really touched my heart. No matter what happens in life, we shouldn't question God—just keep the faith.'

'That's why God has chosen these people,' says Jilani. 'They have faith.'

'So many people ask God "why", but our minister says that we should never ask "why". We should ask "what now?"' says Natasha.

'Noah simply listens to God and obeys him,' Mr Coles agrees.

'So what'll happen now, sir?' asks Sarah. 'Are we going to watch him build the boat? When did this all happen, according to your time machine?'

'One question at a time,' laughs Mr Coles. 'The machine here says that the building of the ark happened 5,000 years ago. I'm afraid there is no way that we have time to watch him build the whole ark, but we can stop and take a look at different stages of the building.'

'Here, sir,' says Steven. 'How big is this boat going to be? I know God mentioned all those figures, but can you explain it a little more simply?'

'Well, Steven,' Mr Coles begins, 'I know that you're a good sprinter. Imagine you are running the 100 metres, and then add on 33 metres, which is like another third added on to your race. Well, that's how long the boat will be. If you then imagine the main building of our school, with four floors, and maybe add another floor, that's how wide the boat will be. If you then imagine seven of me all stood on top of one another, that's how high the boat will be.'

'Sir,' giggles Bronagh, 'just one of you is enough. We don't want to imagine seven of you!'

'Ha ha,' says Mr Coles, trying to think of something clever to say back. 'To sum up then, Steven,' he concludes, 'I reckon you'd be able to get nearly a thousand London buses on the boat!'

'Is that the new bendy ones,' jokes Jilani, 'or the old double-deckers?'

'I was talking about the old double-deckers!' Mr Coles replies. 'Anyway, moving on. What we'll do now is go forward a few weeks, and check what progress there is on the boat building.'

'It does seem really strange, sir,' says Doyin, 'building a boat here, with no water in sight. If I was Noah's daughter, I'd be a little worried at first, in case my dad had gone mad!'

'I suppose that is what real faith is all about,' Mr Coles responds. 'Well, let's move on a few weeks, and check out what's happening.' He adjusts the dial, and before they know it, they are there.

When the pupils look out of the window, they can see a huge pile of tree trunks, and Noah and his family are at work, preparing the wood. The area they have marked out is huge. As Mr Coles described, it is 133 metres long and 22 metres wide, about the size of four or five football pitches. As well as Noah and his family all slaving away, they notice quite a crowd of people standing and watching, and from the expressions on their faces, most of them are being abusive.

Mr Coles opens the minibus door, and the class step out to take a closer look. Noah and his sons are using a basic saw to cut the wood they need. Other members of the family are sanding down some long planks. It is clearly back-breaking work. They can also hear the people in the crowd making fun of the family.

'Come and jump in for a swim, Noah, the water's lovely!' shouts one. The rest of the crowd laugh and jeer.

'Always thought you were a little odd, but now you've gone totally mad!' shouts someone else.

Ham says to Noah, 'Let me sort them out! I'm fed up with hearing their comments every day.'

'Just let it be,' says Noah placidly. 'You have to remember what punishment awaits these people.'

Ham sighs, nods, and continues his work.

'I don't know how they manage to ignore those idiots,' says Alan. 'I'd just pick up one of those pieces of wood and knock their blocks off!'

'Then you'd be as bad as them,' says Shaheda.

'Who cares?' Alan snaps back.

'You would care,' says Bronagh. 'Because if you were a member of this crowd of people, and you behaved like that, then you'd be swimming for your life, like the rest of them will be doing in due course.'

'OK, keep your hair on; I get your point.'

There is something really sad about watching the people hurl abuse at Noah and his family. One or two of the pupils want to walk over and warn them of what awaits them.

'Can we move on a bit into the future now, sir?' asks Bronagh. 'It's not very nice standing here listening to all that abuse.'

'Let's move to the point where all the animals arrive,' adds Jilani. 'That'll be fun!'

The others support Jilani's suggestion, and beg Mr Coles to move them to that point in the story.

'No problem, folks,' says Mr Coles. 'Everybody back on to the bus.' They scramble on board, obviously excited about seeing the animals.

With a few turns of the dial, they arrive. It is quite funny to look out of the window during their brief journey, as out of nowhere a huge boat rises from the ground. It's a bizarre sight.

'That was well wicked,' shouts Alan.

'Everybody out again,' says Mr Coles.

'But we only just got back in!' laughs Natasha. 'This time travel is seriously strange!'

As they emerge, they all stand still, awed at the sight of the ark, which just a few moments ago was nothing but piles of wood spread over the ground.

'No wonder all the people think he's mad,' says Boris. 'Building a massive boat like this in the middle of nowhere!'

'That's faith for you, folks,' says Mr Coles. 'Obeying God's command to build a huge boat in the middle of nowhere, as Boris said, takes a special kind of person with incredible faith.'

'What do you think Noah and his family are up to right now?' asks Shaheda, pointing in the direction of the ark. They all look over and see Noah and his family walking in and out of the boat, carrying hay, fruit, berries and every type of food you can imagine.

'Let's turn to our Bibles again and read the relevant verses to answer Shaheda's question,' says Mr Coles. 'Everyone turn to Genesis chapter 6, verses 19 to 22. John, would you read, please?'

'"Take into the boat with you a male and a female of every kind of animal and of every kind of bird, in order to keep them alive. Take along all kinds of food for you and for them." Noah did everything that God commanded,' John reads out.

'Well, that's your answer, Shaheda,' shouts Jilani. 'They're loading on all the food. Look how much they're taking on board! I've never seen so much food, not even in our local Sainsbury's, and that's a massive store!'

'He's right,' adds Steven. 'There's loads! But where are all the animals? I can't see or hear anything.'

'That's a good question,' says Bronagh. 'And where on earth will Noah find two of every type of animal on the planet?'

'That'll take years,' laughs Sarah. 'The food'll be rotten by then. This doesn't make sense.'

'But remember that Noah has got faith,' says John. 'He knows what he's doing.'

'John is right, you know,' adds Mr Coles. 'Look, Noah and his family are praying now.'

'What do you reckon they're praying for?' asks Alan.

'I reckon they're praying for the answer to Bronagh's question: where on earth are they going to find all these animals?' says Mr Coles.

'Oh my gosh!' screams Sarah. 'Look over there by the trees.'

It is quite unbelievable. Walking towards the boat are two elephants, followed by two rhinos, then donkeys, monkeys, dinosaurs and a whole procession of every imaginable kind of animal behind them.

'They've prayed for a miracle and got one,' laughs Mr Coles, as overwhelmed by this sight as the class are.

Mr Coles ushers the group to move closer, while remaining in the safety of the beam. It is fantastic to watch. Some of the pupils are talking about how they used to sing songs in church or at school about the animals going into the ark two by two, and here it is, for real, happening right in front of their eyes.

'This is so amazing, sir,' says Bronagh. 'How do you think Noah will fit every type of animal in the world on this boat?'

'Bronagh's right,' adds Jilani. 'They'll never manage that!'

'Can I try to answer that question?' asks John. 'I've talked about this at my church youth group.'

'We'd love to hear,' answers Mr Coles. 'Tell us what you've learned at church.'

John continues, 'For a start, just look at those elephants walking on to the boat now; they're babies. In fact, all the animals we've seen are very young.'

'Oh yeah,' says Doyin. 'I never really thought about it, but John's right. It'll be a lot easier to fit them on if they're all little animals.'

'So far, so good, John,' says Mr Coles.

'The other thing we need to remember is that there are so many varieties of one species. Let's take the dog. There are loads of different types of dog, as we know. But not only that; there are also lots of animals that belong in the "dog" family—'

'Like wolves,' shouts Alan.

'Exactly. But not only wolves. You get hyenas, coyotes and—'

'Look!' interrupts Shaheda. 'There are two dog-like animals heading towards the boat now.'

Mr Coles points out, 'And they look as if they're a bit of a mixture between a wolf and a dog. In the future, all different types of canine will descend from these two animals—we can see that now.'

'I can't believe it,' says Boris. 'I have an Alsatian at home. It's incredible to think that my dog descended from those two animals getting on to the boat right now. It's just amazing.'

'Earlier, we saw two donkeys,' continues Mr Coles. 'But they seemed a little bigger than your average donkey. It seems likely that the whole 'horse' family will descend from those two—animals like horses and zebras and all the rest.'

'What about the seahorse?' asks Jilani with a grin.

'You're so stupid,' laughs Natasha.

'From what I have studied over the years,' says Mr Coles, 'I've learnt that there may have been up to 8000 different types of animal represented on the ark.'

'How many animals all together on the boat?' asks Steven.

'Up to 16,000 if there was a pair of each one,' Mr Coles replies, but actually Genesis chapter 7 verse 2 says that Noah took seven pairs of each kind of ritually clean animal, so that means there'd be even more. We can't really be sure.'

'Well,' adds Bronagh, 'if they're quite small, then they really should all be able to fit on this huge boat, and even have a little space to move around.'

As well as Mr Coles and his school group, there is still a large crowd watching everything that's going on, many of them continuing to hurl abuse at Noah and his family. You can see from many of their faces, however, that they are amazed at how all these animals are arriving in pairs, as if by magic. Building a huge boat in the middle of dry land may have seemed the work of a madman, and the jibes and jeers have been understandable. But now, seeing these animals arrive, some of the people are clearly thinking, 'What on earth is happening here?'

A moment or so later, Alan suddenly shouts, 'No! Don't let them on!'

'What on earth are you talking about?' asks Sarah.

'I'm talking about those two wasp-like insects flying towards Noah. A wasp stung me last summer, and it was nasty! Why does Noah have to let creatures like that on the boat? Why can't he say no to things like wasps, ants and cockroaches?'

'People have been bitten by dogs and sharks and other animals,' says Natasha. 'Shall we say no to all of them as well? Besides, honey bees will descend from those 'wasp-like' insects, and I love honey. So I say to Noah, "Bring them on!"'

'They're all God's creatures, you know,' adds Steven. 'They all have a purpose.'

'Yeah, well, suddenly stinging me while I'm walking along minding my own business isn't much of a purpose,' grumbles Alan.

'Seems like a pretty good purpose to me!' laughs Natasha. The others join in the laughter, but Alan just tuts, clearly not amused.

They all go quiet for a few moments, watching the huge array of living creatures heading towards the ark. There are quite a few different birds flying in as well, again in pairs.

'What about all the fish, sir?' asks Jilani. 'When do they all get on?'

'Are you being serious?' asks Boris.

'He is, you know,' grins Bronagh. 'Think about it, Jilani. Why do you think no fish need to get on board—not that they could, anyway?'

'Oh yeah,' nods Jilani. 'Stupid old me. There'll be a flood, so the fish will be OK.'

'Well, folks,' says Mr Coles. It'll take a fair while getting all those animals on board. So let's get back on the bus and move forward in time a little.'

'Are we going straight to the flood now, sir?' Shaheda asks.

'Not yet. We'll just hop forward to see all the animals inside.'

It literally takes a few seconds, and then they find themselves in exactly the same place. The huge boat is still there, with its massive door standing open. But this time, there are no animals in sight. The class can hear all kinds of animal noises coming from the boat, but there are none left outside.

'This is quite eerie,' says Bronagh. 'There aren't even any birds flying around. It's gone so quiet.'

Many of Noah's neighbours have disappeared now too, although there are still a few dozen people standing around. The class hear one of them shout, 'Let's set light to the boat. Then we can have one almighty party.' But apart from these few idiots shouting abuse, everything is still.

'This really is the calm before the storm,' Mr Coles says quietly. 'What is about to happen is going to be absolutely terrifying.'

'Is there going to be a few weeks of rain now, sir?' asks Sarah. 'Is that how the flood comes?'

'I think we're going to be in for a lot more than a few weeks of rain,' Mr Coles answers. 'Let's get back into the bus now. Take one more look around you. This is the last time we'll be seeing the world before the great flood hits it.'

They think about what Mr Coles has said. Some of the pupils look around quite thoughtfully, wondering why this awful thing has to happen so soon after God has created a world of such beauty and wonder. Back on the bus, without Mr Coles having to say so, they all sit in silence. It is a sad moment.

Chapter 14

Everything on earth that breathed died

Mr Coles breaks the silence and asks them to turn to Genesis chapter 7.

'Before we move forward in time again, I would like us to read the Bible account of what is about to happen. Some of you may have a few questions, which we can try to answer. Then we'll move on. Shaheda, could you read for us, please, starting from verse 11.

Shaheda clears her throat.

When Noah was 600 years old, on the seventeenth day of the second month all the outlets of the vast body of water beneath the earth burst open, all the floodgates of the sky were opened, and rain fell on the earth for 40 days and nights. On that same day Noah and his wife went into the boat with their three sons, Shem, Ham, and Japheth, and their wives. With them went every kind of animal, domestic and wild, large and small, and every kind of bird. A male and a female of each kind of living being went into the boat with Noah, as God had commanded. Then the Lord shut the door behind Noah.

The flood continued for 40 days, and the water became deep enough for the boat to float. The water became deeper, and the boat drifted on the surface. It became so deep that it covered the highest mountains; it went on rising until it was about seven metres above the tops of the mountains. Every living being on the earth died—every bird, every animal, and every person. Everything on earth that breathed died. The Lord destroyed all living beings on the earth—human beings, animals, and birds. The only ones left were Noah and those who were with him in the boat. The water did not start going down for 150 days.' [30]

'Well done, Shaheda,' says Mr Coles, 'That was a fairly long passage! As you can all imagine, we are about to witness something devastating. Before we see this great flood and the terrible destruction of life it will cause, does anyone have any questions?'

John puts his hand up and asks, 'What do you think will happen exactly, sir? What I mean is, how do you think this flood will happen? I only ask because I can't see how forty days of rain could be enough to flood the whole earth.'

'John's right, you know,' says Natasha. 'I mean, it rains in England nearly every day, and we don't have a world flood!'

'That is a good point,' responds Mr Coles. 'We need to look back at an important verse from the passage that Shaheda has just read: 'All the outlets of the vast body of water beneath the earth burst open.'[31]

'So what on earth does that mean?' asks Jilani.

'Well, folks,' says Mr Coles, 'I'll try to keep it as simple as I can. At this moment in time, there are no different continents. It's just one big supercontinent. Back in our time, we all know that there isn't just one giant land mass. We have Europe, Africa, America and so on.'

'What's that got to do with the price of eggs?' asks Sarah cheekily.

'If you'd let me continue,' says Mr Coles, 'I'm about to tell you exactly what caused this monster flood. Quite simply, it's this: at the moment there is one supercontinent, but over the next few days and weeks it is going to split up.'

'Do you mean like a big earthquake, sir?' asks Shaheda.

'"Big" is not going to be the word for it. The whole planet is about to have what you might call a "completely devastating" earthquake.'

'Then what are we doing here, sir?' asks Natasha, very concerned. 'We could all die!'

Mr Coles smiles at her reassuringly. 'Now, now. Remember what I said at the beginning of the trip. We are perfectly safe on this minibus. We've already experienced some dodgy conditions outside, and we were fine, so please don't worry.'

'My mum will never believe any of this,' says Natasha shaking her head. 'I've been away from school for a few hours, and I've seen the creation of the planet, dinosaurs, naked people running around, the devil and now I'm about to sit through the largest earthquake this planet has ever experienced!'

'When you put it like that, it sounds quite funny,' laughs Jilani. 'Anyway, we've said already, we won't be telling anyone where we've been, because they'll never believe us.'

'Jilani's right,' says Mr Coles, 'but we'll talk about that later. Let me reassure you all that you have nothing to worry about.'

'So tell us more about this mega earthquake and what's going to happen,' says John.

'I'll try to keep it as simple as before,' says Mr Coles. 'Basically, there's a chain of mid-ocean ridges on the ocean floor, and these ridges connect the oceans. I say ridges, but they are more like fractures in the earth's crust. What's going to happen any time now is that the earth's crust will break into pieces, or what scientists today call plates.'

'We've learnt about them in geography,' says Doyin. 'From what I remember, these plates sometimes collide with other plates and cause earthquakes. I think there is a Pacific plate moving under the western side of the American continent, and that's why you get earthquakes in California.'

'Well done, Doyin,' says Mr Coles. 'I'm glad you've been paying attention in your geography lessons. So, everyone remember: in our time these plates do exist, but at the moment they don't. But they're about to come into existence, and that's what will cause the mighty flood.'

'Oh my gosh, I've just thought,' says Bronagh. 'You know that terrible tragedy that happened on Boxing Day 2004, in Thailand and Indonesia? Is that what we're going to see? A huge tsunami?'

'Bronagh's right,' adds Boris. 'It was caused by an underwater earthquake.'

'That was just two plates that moved into each other,' says Bronagh, 'and look at the awful devastation that caused.'

'I think you're beginning to understand,' Mr Coles responds. 'It's not just a few plates that are going to be moving here. All the underground ridges on the ocean floor that I told you about are going to split. The earth's crust is about to split into many pieces, forming these plates for the first time. This huge split will cause the tsunami that will flood the earth.'

The minibus is silent. All of them still remember the awful images of the Boxing Day tsunami. They are now about to witness something a million times more powerful and destructive.

Tears start to roll down Doyin's face. She looks up and says, 'Suddenly I can't help feeling sorry for those people who are not going to be saved on the ark. I know that the Bible calls them wicked, and I know we saw how awful they were to Noah and his family. But when I think what is about to happen to them, I just can't help feeling sorry for them.'

'She's right,' says Bronagh, putting a comforting arm around Doyin. 'Those pictures we saw on TV are still really clear in our minds, and no matter how awful these people have been, it seems a terrible way to die.'

'If only they could have listened to God,' says Steven. 'Why have they done this to themselves? It's true what Bronagh and Doyin are saying, but as harsh as it sounds, the people have chosen this for themselves. If we were to travel into the future to the day of judgment, we might be saying the same thing about other people. I wish there could be another way, but they've just refused to follow God's way, even though they've had every chance to change their minds.'

They realize that Steven is as upset as Doyin. His eyes have filled with tears. The class are quiet, pondering on what has been said.

John then asks if he can say something. 'Of course,' says Mr Coles, pleased that they are all thinking things through so deeply.

'I just wanted to add to what you've said, sir, about what's going to happen and what causes the flood. I was taught at my church that because of the ridges on the ocean floor splitting, there were huge eruptions under the oceans for thousands and thousands of miles. Because these were so massive, the ocean would have actually started to boil, letting out loads of steam and ash into the air.'

'This is starting to sound worse and worse,' says Natasha, looking increasingly panicked at what she is hearing.

'What John has learned in church is what many believe,' says Mr Coles. 'The non-stop rain, which is also mentioned in the Bible, is a result of all the steam that is about to be released into the atmosphere.'

'Sir,' says Sarah, sounding fed up. 'Can we just get on with it now, because all this technical talk is doing my head in!'

'Maybe Sarah is right,' responds Mr Coles. 'I think we should move forward in time a little and begin to witness for ourselves what actually happens. I'm going to programme the machine to move us a kilometre away from here, to higher ground.' He continues, 'I can also tell you that the minibus will be hovering above the surface at all times. Any quakes, tidal waves or tsunamis will not affect us. You will all be perfectly safe.'

The class are reassured to hear this. Mr Coles adjusts the time machine controls, and within a few seconds the bus has moved to its new location. They can look back at the ark, now a kilometre away, but still a massive sight. Now all the class can do is sit and wait.

As they watch the ark, they suddenly notice the two gigantic doors starting to close. They can't actually see anyone doing this, and Mr Coles informs them that it is the Lord God himself who is causing the doors to close.[32] The people still standing outside gasp in amazement. They have no idea what is happening. Once the doors are fully shut, there is an eerie silence. Jilani tells everyone that he has butterflies in his stomach, and some of the others say that they feel the same. It is that sort of moment.

And then it happens. The first thing they notice is that the people outside the ark start running and screaming. The ground beneath them starts to shake. Many of them lose their balance and fall.

Sarah cries out, 'Listen to that sound!' They can all hear it—a rumble from deep within the earth. They can also hear noises like thunderclaps as the rocks start splitting. To be out in the middle of all that noise must be terrifying.

'The ocean ridges around the planet are beginning to crack. This continent is being torn apart,' says Mr Coles. Cracks and fissures are appearing in the ground wherever they look. As they look on helplessly at the people running away from the ark, they can see some falling into gaping crevasses that open suddenly at their feet. One moment they are running desperately; the next they are swallowed up by the earth.

'Those poor people,' says Doyin. She points at some who are trying to climb up the ark, even as the earth tremors threaten to shake them off. Others are battering on the doors, but with no luck. It would seem that God is the only one who can open and close those huge doors.

'If those people are terrified now,' says Steven quietly, 'imagine what they'll be like when the tsunamis arrive.'

'At least it will be quick,' says Boris. 'I know that sounds cruel, but they won't suffer for long.'

'When will the waves come, sir?' asks Shaheda.

'Well,' says Mr Coles, 'tsunamis normally arrive fairly rapidly after a normal earthquake at sea, but this is different. This is a complete ripping apart of the ocean ridges. I would say that the waves should be here very shortly, and the rain and ash will not be far behind.'

It is awful watching the people outside, trying hopelessly to save themselves. If only they knew what was about to hit them! The quakes intensify. People are being thrown all over the place, and even the ark begins to sway from side to side.

'Oh my God!' screams Sarah. 'Look!' She points at the horizon. It can only be described as a scene from your worst nightmare. The horizon is filled with a black wall, coming towards them incredibly fast. It is utterly terrifying, and it is just one of the mega-tsunamis striking all over the planet. As the water comes closer, Mr Coles says to the group, 'Remember, everyone, our bus is much higher than that wave, so there is no need to be afraid.'

No one responds. They just sit there, mouths open, watching the monster wall of water get closer and closer. In the silence, they begin to hear the roar of the wave. The people left outside the ark can now see and hear it too. Most run screaming for their lives. Others make one last desperate attempt to climb up the side of the ark. None of them has any chance of escape. The water is demolishing everything in its path. Every living thing is being destroyed, instantly.

'That wave is nearly as high as the ark,' says Alan. 'Even the ark will get destroyed.' 'Watch!' says Mr Coles, intent on the scene outside.

The wall of water reaches the ark. Everyone outside, whether running or clambering up the ark, is instantly swept away. The noise outside is deafening, like a thousand waterfalls. The power of the wave is phenomenal.

'That's got to be a miracle!' Steven exclaims. 'The ark should have been demolished when the wave hit.'

'I think you're right,' says Mr Coles. 'The speed and height of that mountain of water would have destroyed any modern-day ship, whether oil tanker or battleship. Noah's ark is only made of wood, and yet it's suffered absolutely no damage.'

It's true: when the wave struck the ark, it hardly moved, but just started to float on the water. As the class continue to watch, a surreal landscape is formed. All the land has disappeared, and there is nothing but ocean as far as they can see. What was once a huge supercontinent has been ripped apart, and every bit of land is now submerged under water. Every living being on earth has been destroyed.

Bronagh, her eyes full of tears, says, 'This is such a terrible thing to witness. Not long ago, we were in the beautiful garden of Eden, seeing God's creation at its best. Now, because of the way people have behaved, we see God's destructive power at its worst.'

'Bronagh is right,' says Doyin. 'Out of all the people in the world, it was only Noah and his family who were good and faithful. All that's left of humanity is on that boat. It's so sad.'

To add to the bleakness of the situation, the sky starts to turn very dark, saturated with moisture and ash.

'Great,' says Jilani. 'This is all we need to cheer us up.' As he says this, it starts to pour with rain, absolutely chucking it down. The noise inside the bus is deafening. It is raining so hard that you can't really distinguish the raindrops. It is like sitting under a waterfall, but because of the amount of ash in the atmosphere, the rain is a filthy grey colour.

'Do you think the Boxing Day tsunami was also a punishment from God?' asks Doyin.

'Absolutely not!' Mr Coles responds immediately. 'Sadly, that was a result of natural movements of the earth's plates. It's like hurricanes and tornadoes: they are all part of nature, and sadly people do die. You must never think that God punishes people when these terrible but natural occurrences take place.'

Chapter 15

A new beginning

Mr Coles says to the group, 'It's going to be like this for quite a while now. There's no point us hanging around here, as we really can't see a thing. The rain will continue, and the water will keep rising. I think it will be best for us to move forward in time a little.'

'Sir,' says Jilani, 'can we actually get inside the ark, just to see what's happening on board?'

'Yeah, that'll be fun,' adds Sarah.

'It'll smell a bit,' laughs Alan. 'All that animal poo!'

'Trust you to come up with something like that,' says Bronagh.

Mr Coles quietens them down and says, 'I'll move us forward to the moment when the ark comes to rest on a mountain in the Ararat range. I'll also get the minibus to stop on the front end of the ark. There is some space there, and we won't be seen as long as we all stay within the beam.'

Mr Coles sets the coordinates, and they shift forward in time. They immediately know that they are on board the ark, because they can feel themselves swaying.

Shaheda says straight away, 'I don't like this. I'll be sick!'

John offers her some water, which she accepts gladly.

Mr Coles tells the group that if anyone does feel seasick, they should let him know, as he will direct them to the side of the boat where they can be sick to their heart's content. 'Very soon, the ark will ground on the top of a mountain, so you might get jolted a little. But you can get out of the bus and walk around now, so long as you remember to stay within the safety beam.'

It feels good to get outside again. The rain has stopped, the sun is shining, and the sea is now relatively calm. Boris is the first one to venture off towards the boundary set by the beam. He finds a small door and opens it. Excited by what he sees inside, he calls the others over. As they peer in, they can see elephants, rhinos and a whole variety of other animals.

'They all look so calm,' says Bronagh.

'Wow,' says Sarah. 'This is wicked! They've got a lot more room than I thought they would have.'

Jilani says, 'Alan wasn't wrong about the smell!'

'I did tell you it would pong a little,' laughs Alan.

'Hey, look,' says John. 'That's one of Noah's sons—Shem, I think. It looks like he's about to feed some of the animals.'

Shem is throwing in what looks like cabbages and turnips to the elephants, who munch away happily.

'It's amazing how tame the animals seem to be,' says Steven. 'Shem is able to stroke and pat each one of them.'

'I think that's another example of a miracle,' says Natasha. 'God is protecting Noah and his family, and that includes protection from the animals as well.'

'I reckon you're right,' Bronagh replies.

As they're chatting, they suddenly hear a huge creaking and grinding noise. There is a bump, and some of the group fall to the floor. Mr Coles checks that everyone is OK.

'What was that?' asks Shaheda nervously.

Mr Coles answers, 'The boat has obviously come to a rest on one of the mountains in the Ararat range, just as it says in Genesis.' [33]

'But sir,' says Natasha, 'we haven't seen any mountains in all the time we've been travelling. This supercontinent that we've been travelling around seemed quite flat to me. So where have these mountains come from?'

'I can answer that,' says John.

'Go, Professor John!' says Jilani.

John continues, 'These mountains have been formed because of the splitting and collision of all the plates.'

'That's correct,' says Mr Coles.

As they're discussing this, Noah and his family appear and rush excitedly to the side of the boat. You can tell by looking at their faces that they're experiencing a tremendous sense of relief. After all this time on the ark in the rain, they now can feel dry land beneath them. They are still surrounded by water, and there is a long way to go before they are safe, but this is a start. Noah then points into the distance. Mr Coles and the group all look in the same direction. On the horizon, they can see mountain peaks. The water is slowly subsiding.

Mr Coles says to the group, 'OK, listen, everybody. I suggest we go back to the minibus now. It's going to be a good month or two before the waters really subside and they can leave the ark. Let's get back inside the bus, read the next part of the story in Genesis, and we'll then decide which point to travel to next.'

'Sir, how much longer before we need to be back at school?' asks Boris.

'We need to be back at school by soon after four, which gives us another couple of hours,' answers Mr Coles.

He hands them all a Bible, and asks Jilani to read Genesis chapter 8, verses 6 to 19. They turn to the passage, and Jilani begins:

After 40 days Noah opened a window and sent out a raven. It did not come back, but kept flying around until the water was completely gone. Meanwhile, Noah sent out a dove to see if the water had gone down, but since the water still covered all the land, the dove did not find a place to alight—

Jilani pauses. 'What does "alight" mean?'

'That's a fair question, as it's not a word that is used much,' answers Mr Coles. 'It means to land, or set down.'

'Cheers, sir.' Jilani continues.

It flew back to the boat, and Noah reached out and took it in. He waited another seven days and sent out the dove again. It returned to him in the evening with a fresh olive leaf in its beak. So Noah knew that the water had gone down. Then he waited another seven days and sent out the dove once more; this time it did not come back.

When Noah was 601 years old, on the first day of the first month, the water was gone. Noah removed the covering of the boat, looked round, and saw that the ground was getting dry. By the twenty-seventh day of the second month the earth was completely dry.

God said to Noah, 'Go out of the boat with your wife, your sons, and their wives. Take all the birds and animals out with you, so that they may reproduce and spread over all the earth.' So Noah went out of the boat with his wife, his sons, and their wives. All the animals and birds went out of the boat in groups of their own kind.

'OK, Jilani,' says Mr Coles. 'That was very well read.'

'Naturally!' laughs Jilani.

Bronagh comments, 'It took Noah a long time before he was able to leave the boat. Why didn't he just get out when the dove returned with the olive branch?'

John answers her. 'The earth may have been drying out, but it must have still been really soggy and muddy. With all this water, it's bound to take a while before the ground is properly dry.'

'That's right,' says Mr Coles. 'Noah was a wise man. If he'd released the animals too early, they'd have become bogged down, and may never have survived. Noah has to be patient. I reckon we should move forward to the point where they are able to leave the boat. Is everyone happy with that?'

They all nod in agreement.

With a twiddle of the dial, it's not long before they get there.

'Wow,' says Sarah. 'The whole world suddenly looks so different.'

Sarah is right. The water has gone, and in every direction there are mountain ranges. The ark is high up on one peak, and down below they can see into some valleys, which look green and beautiful. Mr Coles asks them to step out of the bus straight away, as it is such a beautiful day. It is wonderful for the class to see land again, and even more so for Noah and his family who have been cooped up in the ark for so long.

The class take another look at the ark. When it was first built, it seemed strange just resting on dry ground. It now looks even more bizarre, resting halfway up a mountain, but it has done its job perfectly. It has saved Noah and his family, and all the animals, for this moment in time—a new beginning.

Just as the huge doors on the ark had miraculously closed before the flood, so now they suddenly start to creak open. It is certainly God doing this again, as there is no way that anyone else could have shifted them. The group stand and stare, some with their mouths open wide. They have seen some incredible things on this trip so far, but they never cease to be amazed, every step of the way.

Once the doors are wide open, Noah and his family clamber out of the ark and on to dry land. No sooner have they done this than they start to laugh and dance around. It is wonderful to see.

'This is great,' says Doyin. 'I feel like joining in with them.'

'I'd have danced as well,' laughs Bronagh.

Noah's sons are picking up handfuls of soil and throwing it at each other. They are having a great time. There must have been many occasions on the boat when they doubted whether they would ever see land again. But they have kept their faith in God, and this is their reward.

Noah and his family eventually calm down, and start to look around at their new surroundings. The group can see them pointing down into the valleys, obviously agreeing that that is where they may head for, to set up their new home.

Then the class hear Noah say, 'It is now time to release the animals so that they can go out and reproduce and spread over the land.' He gives instructions to different family members, and they head back into the boat. Within a few moments, hundreds of birds, all different shapes and sizes, come flying out of the ark and head toward the valleys. It is a spectacular sight.

'Here come some frogs!' shouts Jilani.

'I can see some foxes,' says Doyin.

Eventually they can't keep up their commentary. The animals just come pouring out, running in every direction, but staying in their pairs.

'Here come man's best friend,' says Boris. He points at the dog-like creatures. They are the only two animals that don't run off. In fact, Shem comes out of the ark and both dogs jump up at him. He strokes them and plays with them for a while.

'So, right from the beginning, humans and dogs get on well together!' says Mr Coles.

Then some dinosaur creatures of different shapes and sizes come out of the ark.

'Look at them,' says Bronagh. 'They seem a bit confused, and don't know which way to go.'

'I think that helps to explain why they eventually became extinct!' adds John.

'Why do you say that?' asks Mr Coles.

'Well, look at them. The land is now totally different. Perhaps the other animals are OK and will survive this new terrain, but I don't think these huge beasts are going to find it so easy.'

'You could be right,' says Bronagh. 'So it's thanks to people that these magnificent beasts become extinct.'

'What are you on about?' asks Jilani.

Bronagh continues, 'It's quite simple. Because people were wicked and turned away from God, he destroyed the world with this great flood. But as a result, the earth became so different that the dinosaurs couldn't survive in it. So it's the fault of humans that they became extinct.'

'Even back here, we're having a negative effect on creation,' sighs Doyin.

Pretty soon, the ark is empty. It took ages to get the animals on to the ark, but it seems to take no time getting them all off. Apart from the two dogs, the animals finally start making their way down into the valleys.

'I wonder how Noah and his family are feeling at this moment,' murmurs Shaheda.

'Well,' says John, 'over the last few months they've seen the destruction of their world, and now they must be wondering what the future holds.'

'If we watch now,' says Mr Coles, 'we will see and hear God

confirming to Noah and his family that they do have a future. Basically, the world is going to begin again in the same way as before.'

They notice that Noah and his family are gathering rocks and piling them up.

'What's going on now?' asks Alan.

'He's making an altar,' calls Jilani. 'I read a little further on in Genesis, and it says that Noah builds an altar to offer a sacrifice to the Lord.'

'Well done,' says Mr Coles. 'You're always full of surprises.'

'Usually stupid surprises,' mutters Shaheda under her breath.

'I heard that,' laughs Jilani.

After a while, the altar is built. Noah and his family then pile up plenty of wood on top, starting with small pieces, and ending with thick logs.

'That'll be one heck of a fire,' says Alan.

'Well,' says Mr Coles, 'he's about to sacrifice a fair few animals on that altar, and he's going to need a fair old fire to do it.'

'But all the animals have disappeared,' says Alan. 'Does he have to go down into the valleys and find some? And when he does find some, they'll become extinct because he'll have killed them.'

'That's a good point,' says Mr Coles. 'But if you remember, at the start of Genesis chapter 7 God tells Noah to bring on board seven pairs of each kind of ritually clean animal.'

'Oh, so he's got some spare ones tucked away, then?' asks Alan.

'Yes, in a nutshell,' answers Mr Coles.

'Why are they in a nutshell?' asks Jilani.

'Ha ha,' says Bronagh sarcastically.

The wood has been piled up, and Noah crouches down to light the fire. Within a minute or two, it is burning nicely. Meanwhile, Ham has collected the ritually clean animals from the ark. There are some lambs and pigeons.

Mr Coles tells the group, 'I would look away now if I were you, as Noah and his sons are about to slit the throats of the animals.'

Most of the group looks away, but one or two of them keep an eye on the proceedings. The throats are cut, the blood is drained, and the animals are thrown whole on to the fiery altar. It is not a pretty sight!

'This reminds me of the foot-and-mouth outbreak, when all the animals had to be burned,' says Bronagh, looking rather disgusted.

The smoke rises way above them into the sky, and once again they hear the voice of God in their own language.

Never again will I put the earth under a curse because of what people do; I know that from the time they are young their thoughts are evil. Never again will I destroy all living beings, as I have done this time. As long as the world exists, there will be a time for planting and a time for harvest. There will always be cold and heat, summer and winter, day and night.' [34]

'So this is the new beginning,' says Natasha.

'Is it really like it was in the very beginning again?' asks Jilani. 'The way it was with Adam and Eve?'

'That's a very good question,' says Mr Coles, 'but the truth is that God is not reversing the curse. Sadly, sin is still in the world, and the ground is still going to produce thorns! But even so, it is a new beginning for Noah and his family, and God is certainly not going to take drastic action again and flood the whole planet.'

'It seems to be that God accepts that we are all sinners,' adds John.

'Nicely put,' says Mr Coles.

'I noticed that when we heard God speak just now, he mentioned that it is our thoughts that are evil,' says Doyin.

'That's a good point, you know,' adds Bronagh, 'because that's where I reckon most sinning goes on!'

'Too true!' says Mr Coles. 'It's not just what we do that counts with God. It's really all about what we're thinking.'

'I'm doomed, then!' sighs Alan.

'Well, at least you're honest about it,' says Natasha, 'and that's what counts.'

Mr Coles continues, 'There are many people who seem to be

doing good things, but often their thoughts are bad, or they're doing things for selfish reasons.'

'You know,' says Steven, 'there's a verse in the Bible—I think it's in 1 Samuel—where Samuel is searching for the next king of Israel, and he only thinks about how Jesse's sons look. Samuel goes through all of them, but God rejects each one. Eventually, it's the youngest son, David, who is chosen. God tells Samuel that "people look at the outward appearance, but I look at the heart".'[35]

'That's brilliant, Steven,' says Mr Coles, patting him on the back. 'That is such an appropriate verse for this situation.'

The rest of the group starts patting him on the back too.

'OK, OK,' says Steven. 'I know I'm brilliant!'

Shaheda then adds, 'In Islam, we talk about God being the merciful and the forgiving. We are lucky that God does have a merciful heart compared to our evil hearts.'

'Amen to that!' shouts Natasha.

'Another brilliant point,' says Mr Coles. 'You're all doing so well today!'

As they stand there watching the burning of the sacrifice, Mr Coles makes another comment. 'The last thing that God promises Noah is that there will be seasons, and that food will grow and life will carry on. Noah and his family have bowed down to God in worship, and he in turn has promised to provide for them.'

'Where's the rainbow, sir?' asks Sarah. 'I remember there was a great big rainbow in this story somewhere.'

'That's a good point,' says Mr Coles, 'and it will be appearing very soon. In fact, it's a good time to mention this, because in a few minutes we'll have to think about getting back to our own time, and returning to school.'

'Oh sir, please,' they all moan.

'This has been such a wicked adventure,' sighs Alan. 'I can't believe we have to go.'

'We don't,' says Boris. 'We could stay here for weeks, or years, and still get back to school at the right time.'

'Let's not start that discussion again,' says Mr Coles emphatically, still not wishing to get bogged down in the details of time travel. He continues, 'I will make a promise here and now, though.'

'Go on then, sir,' they say in unison.

'I promise that there will be other adventures like this, just for you ten. We can plan another one quite soon. How does that sound?'

'Nice one, sir!' says Jilani.

Others shout, 'Wicked!'

'Well, on that note,' continues Mr Coles 'let's have no more fuss about having to leave soon. We still have a little time. I notice that the sacrificial fire is dying down now, and I do believe that God is about to speak to Noah again to make a special agreement with him. Let's sit down quietly and listen. It may take a minute or two.'

They all find a place to sit down, fairly close to the altar. Then God's voice fills the air.

Have many children, so that your descendants will live all over the earth. All the animals, birds, and fish will live in fear of you. They are all placed under your power. Now you can eat them, as well as green plants; I give them all to you for food. The one thing you must not eat is meat with blood still in it; I forbid this because the life is in the blood. If anyone takes human life, he will be punished. I will punish with death any animal that takes a human life. Human beings were made like God, so whoever murders one of them will be killed by someone else.

You must have many children, so that your descendants will live all over the earth. I am now making my covenant with you and with your descendants, and with all living beings—all birds and all animals— everything that came out of the boat with you. With these words I make my covenant with you: I promise that never again will all living beings be destroyed by a flood; never again will a flood destroy the earth. As a sign of this everlasting covenant which I am making with you and with all living beings, I am putting my bow in the clouds. It will be a sign of my covenant with the world. Whenever I cover the sky with clouds and the rainbow appears, I will remember my promise to you and to all the animals that a flood will never again destroy all living beings. When the rainbow appears in the clouds, I will see it and remember the everlasting covenant between

me and all living beings on earth. That is the sign of the promise which I
am making to all living beings.[36]

'It still amazes me that we're actually hearing God speak,' says Alan.

'It's incredible,' Bronagh agrees.

'You know,' adds Boris, 'listening to God just then, it sounded like Genesis chapter 1 all over again—all that stuff about "have many children", and "you're in charge of the animals".'

'That's a very good point,' says Mr Coles. 'In a way, God the creator is beginning again, and he is reinstating humankind to be his representatives on earth.'

'People can eat meat now, though,' says Jilani.

'That's right,' continues Mr Coles. 'It seems that since Adam and Eve sinned, meat-eating has already been going on. But God does give some very strict instructions about not eating the blood of any animal.'

'Does that include black pudding?' asks Alan.

'That's disgusting,' says Jilani, sounding repulsed by the idea.

'So what's wrong with eating the blood, sir?' Alan continues. 'Why has God made it such a strict rule?'

'It's quite simple,' Mr Coles replies. 'The blood basically represents the life. Whatever people eat, it is a gift from God. Humans must always remember that God is still Lord over them, so part of this food is forbidden to them. They must not eat it. The blood, in a way, symbolizes the life that he gave to the animals, and all life belongs to God.'

'Sir,' says Natasha, 'is this a bit like God telling Adam not to eat the fruit from the tree of knowledge of good and evil?'

'Well done, Natasha.' Mr Coles answers. 'That is a very good comparison. Every command is still a test of people's obedience.'

'God also went on about not killing people as well, didn't he, sir?' says Steven.

'It must have been because of what happened between Cain and Abel,' says Shaheda.

'I was thinking the same thing,' adds Bronagh.

'We're made in God's image,' says Doyin, 'so we can't kill each other. We all represent God here on earth; he is part of us all. To kill a fellow human being is to rebel against God, who is our Creator.'

As they are discussing this, Sarah shouts and points to the sky. 'Wow! Look at that rainbow.'

She is right. It is spectacular.

'I've seen rainbows many times,' continues Sarah, 'but this one is so bright and so clear.'

'It looks as though you could run up to it and touch it,' says Jilani, also impressed with its beauty and size.

'What a wonderful sight,' says Bronagh. 'Perfect for a new beginning.'

They all stand and stare for a while. Of course they have seen rainbows before, but this one is perfect. It isn't necessarily the first ever rainbow on earth, but it is surely the most beautiful.

Mr Coles then looks at his watch and realizes that they need to be making their way back to school. He says to the group, 'OK, everyone, as I mentioned before, it is about time we started heading home. But what I thought we might do, as we have a little more time, is to take a whistlestop tour of some of the rest of Genesis.'

'What sort of tour is one of those?' asks Sarah.

'Well, basically it means that I will stop the minibus for a minute or two at other well-known stories from Genesis. We'll make it like a quiz. Each time I stop somewhere, you have to look out of the window and guess what moment in time we are at.'

'Sounds like fun, sir,' says Shaheda.

'So let's get back on board, then,' says Mr Coles enthusiastically. 'Whoever correctly guesses where we have stopped will be awarded a merit point!' The pupils are excited by this. Jilani shouts out, 'Come on, then, sir. I've got 48 merits already. I only need two more to reach 50; then I get my prize and certificate.'

'You've got no chance,' says Alan. 'We'll all guess the answers well before you.'

'We'll see,' Jilani replies.

Chapter 16

The whistlestop tour home

Mr Coles tells the group that he has set the dials for their next destination, and that they are ready to leave. Everyone has a final look at Noah and his family.

Doyin shouts, 'Good luck, Noah!'

'Why do you say that?' asks Boris. 'We know what happens next.'

'I just felt it was the right thing to say,' Doyin answers.

'OK, everyone, here goes,' says Mr Coles. As usual, everything outside begins to blur for a few seconds, and then refocuses. 'We're here!' he shouts. 'Everybody out.'

As they step down from the minibus, they see hundreds of people at work two or three hundred metres away. Many of them are trampling in the mud while others are throwing in straw.

'Anybody got any idea what might be happening here?' asks Mr Coles.

'Mud wrestling!' says Alan. They all laugh.

Bronagh says, 'They're making bricks. They always used to use a mixture of mud and straw.'

'Well done,' says Mr Coles. 'Now look at those people on the right. What are they doing? And, for one merit, who can tell me what it is we are looking at?'

They all look over to the right, where there are hundreds of men laying bricks, building some kind of tower.

'That's it!' shouts Natasha. 'That building is a tower. It's that story about those people who wanted to be flash and build a tower that could reach God. It's the tower of Babel!'

'Correct!' shouts Mr Coles. 'That's one merit for you!'

'Yeah!' shouts Natasha.

'I was going to say the tower of Babel,' grumbles Jilani.

'Yeah, yeah,' say the rest of them.

'Their silly pride gets them into trouble,' says John.

'Then God mixes up their languages,' adds Sarah. 'I remember this story now.'

'OK, class, it's time for us to leave,' says Mr Coles. 'Remember, we have to be quick if we want to stop at other places as well.'

'Yeah,' says Jilani, 'let's move. I need to get two merits!'

They scramble back on to the bus, all enjoying this little game that Mr Coles has devised. Once they are aboard, off they go to their next destination.

The minibus has come to rest on quite a high mountain.

'Where are we now?' asks Alan.

'One of you will work it out soon,' Mr Coles replies.

They get out of the bus and look down into the valley below. In the light of the rising sun they can see two cities there. Nobody says anything. They are all waiting for more information!

'Is this it?' asks Shaheda. 'Do we get no more clues than this?'

'These two cities themselves should be a good clue, but let's wait to see what happens now,' says Mr Coles.

The beautiful sunrise over the valley suddenly changes, and looks like a scene from hell.

'What on earth is happening?' shouts Alan.

Massive fireballs have started falling from the sky and landing on the two cities. Even from up on the mountain, the noise is deafening—huge explosions, distant screams. Within a few moments both cities are destroyed. It is like watching a Second World War air raid. Everyone is too shocked to speak. They just stand and stare at the devastation.

'Look over there!' calls out Sarah. 'Some people have survived.'

She is right. Fleeing from the devastation are a man and three women, climbing up from the valley.

'I've got it!' shouts Boris. 'This is the story where God destroys the two cities of Sodom and Gomorrah, and if I remember right, one of those women—'

'Is about to turn into a pillar of salt,' interrupts Jilani.

They all watch the four fleeing figures. One of the women stops, and looks round at the devastated cities. Within seconds of doing so, she just turns into a pillar of salt. It is a bizarre and terrible thing to observe.

'That merit is awarded to Boris, as he was the first to start speaking,' says Mr Coles.

'But sir,' moans Jilani, 'I got the salt bit right.'

'Yes, you did, and you are getting closer to earning your merit. But you need to be the first one to give the answer.'

Jilani pulls a sulky face.

'Once again, well done, Boris,' says Mr Coles. 'The inhabitants of these two cities were a nasty bunch, and very inhospitable to strangers.'

'I did like those firebombs,' says Alan. 'They were well cool!'

'You're sick!' says Natasha, scowling at him.

'Yes, well, let's get back on board now,' says Mr Coles. 'Let's see who will guess the next one first. It may be you, Jilani!'

When they reach their next destination, Jilani is the first one out of the bus, looking all around for clues in the bleak, rocky landscape.

'There's a pile of stones over there with some wood on top,' says Steven, pointing to the right.

'It looks like a kind of altar,' says Bronagh, 'the same sort of thing that Noah built after the flood.'

As they consider the altar, they hear voices. Then an elderly, bearded man and a young boy emerge from behind a rock, walking towards them. The old man is carrying embers in a clay pot. A second later, the silence is broken by a triumphant yell. It is Jilani. 'I've got it! I've got it!'

'Go on, then,' says Mr Coles. 'Tell us all where we are and what we're looking at.'

'That old geezer is Abraham, and the young lad is his son Isaac. Abraham has been told by God to sacrifice his only son.'

'Well done, Jilani,' says Mr Coles. 'You have earned your merit.'

Jilani is extremely chuffed.

'Well done, Jilani,' says Natasha. 'That should stop you sulking.'

'Can we stay and watch this for a while?' asks John. 'It's one of my favourite Bible passages, and I'd love to see what happens.'

'Me too,' says Doyin.

Mr Coles agrees, so they stay there, keeping a close eye on Abraham and his son. When the man and boy reach the altar, Mr Coles and his class can hear what they are saying.

'Father,' says Isaac.

'Yes, Isaac?' answers Abraham.

'We're off to make a sacrifice, but we don't seem to have a lamb. You've got the coals and wood, but where's the lamb?' asks Isaac.

'Don't worry about it,' says Abraham. 'God will provide us with one.'

When they get to the altar, Abraham turns and starts tying up his son. Then he lifts him carefully on top of the wood on the altar.

'It's amazing,' says John. 'I always imagined that Isaac would've made a real fuss at this point, wondering if his father had totally cracked up.'

'If this sort of thing happened nowadays,' says Sarah, 'the social services would be straight round!'

The others laugh at this.

'It's a fair point that John has made,' says Mr Coles. 'It is not just Abraham who demonstrates real faith here, but also young Isaac. The boy doesn't object or question his father at all.'

'Sir, we also have this story in the Qur'an,' says Jilani. 'In our version it is about Abraham and Ishmael, but the story is the same. It's all about faith. Anyway, in our story, Ishmael asks to be put face down on the altar, so that Abraham won't be able to see his face and be tempted not to carry out God's command.'

'Thanks for that, Jilani,' says Mr Coles. 'I never knew that, but it certainly highlights that it was not just Abraham who demonstrated faith.'

They all go quiet and watch the action. Abraham looks up to the sky. He then lifts his knife, utters a few words and seems to be about to make a downward thrust into the body of Isaac, when they all hear a loud voice, apparently coming out of thin air: 'Don't hurt the boy or do anything to him. Now I know that you honour and obey God, because you have not kept back your only son from him.'[37]

A while later, Abraham sacrifices a ram, which God has told him to find in a bush nearby. Abraham and Isaac stand and watch the flames of the sacrifice. They then embrace each other and start on their journey home.

'It was great to see this,' says Bronagh. 'I remember when we did some drama in class based on this story. It's amazing to see that it's just how it was written in the Bible.'

'Well,' says Mr Coles. 'The merit goes to Jilani, for working it out before anybody else. Let's get back into the bus. We may be able to make a few more stops, and then I'm afraid it's back to school.'

They rush on board, eagerly anticipating the next stop. When it's time to get out again, the first thing they see is a huge group of people sitting round a large fire. In the centre of the group is a fairly elderly man, while seated alongside him are younger men and women. There are children playing all over the place.

'This is a tricky one,' says Boris. 'This could be a group of anybody.'

'Keep watching,' says Mr Coles. 'You'll guess it in due course.'

They carry on watching the group, who are sharing a meal with much laughter and good-humoured conversation. After some time, the elderly man claps his hands loudly. The group falls silent, until the only sound to be heard is the crackling of the fire in the middle of the circle. The elderly man then claps his hands again. Some men, possibly servants, come running before him, carrying a large and beautifully decorated piece of cloth. As they hold it up, the class realize that it is a coat of some kind.

'I've worked it out,' calls Shaheda.

'Same here,' shout many of the others, but Shaheda was first.

'OK, Shaheda,' says Mr Coles. 'Tell us where you think we are and what exactly is going on.'

'Well,' says Shaheda, clearing her throat. 'That elderly man in the middle must be Jacob. All the other men sitting near him are his sons. The servants have just brought a beautiful coat to Jacob, which he is now about to give to his favourite son, Joseph.'

'Brilliant!' shouts Mr Coles. 'You've worked it out perfectly. One merit for you. Let's see what happens when he gives the coat to Joseph.'

'I reckon that's Joseph over there,' says Sarah, pointing at a good-looking young man sitting to the immediate right of Jacob.

'I think you've got it,' says Bronagh. 'I remember the Bible describing him as handsome, and I think he really is.'

'Calm down, ladies,' says Mr Coles.

Jacob asks Joseph to stand up, and the servants place the robe over him. It looks magnificent.

'Remember, it was very unusual for someone to own such a coat,' says Mr Coles. 'It is an amazingly generous gift.'

'Look at their faces,' laughs Jilani, pointing at Joseph's brothers. 'They're not a happy bunch.'

Jilani is right. They look furious. Are they jealous? You bet they are!

'You can understand why they're so annoyed, though,' says Natasha. 'I'd be well angry!'

'Me too,' says Alan. 'It isn't right for a parent to have favourites. I should know. My little sister is spoilt rotten. I get the blame for everything!'

'Poor you,' says Sarah.

'Yeah, well it isn't fair,' says Alan, really starting to grumble now.

'Parents shouldn't have favourites, you're right,' says John. 'But here it was all part of God's plan. Because they all hated Joseph and were so jealous of him, they ended up selling him into slavery.'

'That's right,' Bronagh continues. 'He ends up in Egypt, and to cut a long story short, it's thanks to Joseph that his family don't die of starvation. It was all part of God's master plan. They end up happily ever after, anyway.'

'That was a very short summary,' says Mr Coles. 'Thanks for that.'

'Any time,' say John and Bronagh simultaneously.

Mr Coles looks at his watch. 'We really do need to set off back to school now. I did say that this would be a whistlestop tour on the way home. We really have to leave now, so please get back on the minibus.'

They all do so, but not over-enthusiastically. The whole class is sad that this wonderful adventure is now coming to a close.

Once they are all seated, Mr Coles can see how gloomy their faces are. He says to them, 'I know how disappointed you are now, but remember, I did promise that we will make another trip back in time very soon.'

'But once the rest of the school find out where we've been, they'll all want to go, and we won't have a chance,' moans Jilani.

'But don't you remember Bronagh's plan?' grins Mr Coles. 'Nobody is going to believe where we've been, and if we do try to convince them, they'll think that we're totally mad. So we were going to tell everyone that we've been looking at some old country churches.'

'Nice plan, though I say so myself,' laughs Bronagh.

'But isn't that lying?' asks Natasha.

'Not really,' says Mr Coles. 'We did pass a few old churches when we drove through Essex at the beginning of the trip.'

'Yeah,' says Bronagh. 'I remember them. They were quite beautiful.'

'Great,' says Alan. 'When you arrange the next trip, just tell people that it's to go and look at old country churches. No one else will want to come, so the ten of us will get the places again. Sneaky one, sir!'

'Good, so we are all agreed,' says Mr Coles.

He tells them that he is programming the time machine to take them straight back to school. 'The bus will arrive in the quiet road at the back of school. No one will see us. Have you all enjoyed your journey?'

'This hasn't been any ordinary school trip,' says Alan. 'I've never believed in any of this Bible stuff, but what I've seen over the last few hours has blown my mind. I'm convinced—there really is a God!'

Mr Coles adjusts the time machine dials for the last time. As usual, everything outside turns into a blur, and before they know it, they are parked next to their school. It's exactly four o'clock. Perfect timing! They all thank Mr Coles for a brilliant trip.

'See you tomorrow,' says Mr Coles.

'Maybe tomorrow, or maybe yesterday,' laughs Jilani.

'Can't we send Jilani back in time and leave him there?' laughs Sarah.

Mr Coles has a brief look around, pops his head back into the bus, unscrews the time machine device and places it inside his rucksack. He then closes and locks the door. At that moment, the head teacher walks up behind him and asks, 'Good trip, Mike?'

'Unbelievable,' Mr Coles replies. 'The kids were great.'

'I've seen some of them,' says the head. 'They told me it was the best school trip they have ever been on. Who'd have thought a bunch of East End kids would love a day out looking at old church buildings? Well done, Mike. Let's hope you run another trip soon.'

'I'd love to,' Mr Coles replies. 'I'd absolutely love to.'

Mr Coles heads towards the staffroom with his rucksack.

'Old church buildings,' he mutters to himself, and smiles.

NOTES

1   Genesis 1:1–2
2   Surah 21:30
3   Surah 24:25
4   Genesis 1:9
5   See Genesis 1:10
6   Genesis 1:11
7   Job 38:4
8   Job 40:15–18
9   Job 40:19
10   Genesis 2:16–17
11   Genesis 2:23
12   Matthew 19:4–6
13   Genesis 3:1
14   Genesis 3:2–3
15   Genesis 3:4–5
16   Hebrews 4:13
17   1 Timothy 2:14
18   Genesis 3:10
19   Genesis 3:12–13
20   Genesis 3:14–15
21   Micah 7:17
22   Genesis 3:16
23   Genesis 3:17–19
24   See Genesis 3:20
25   Genesis 3:22
26   Genesis 4:6–7
27   Acts 17:26
28   Thanks to the Sir John Cass's Foundation and Redcoat Church of England secondary school science department for explaining this to me.
29   Genesis 6:13–21
30   Genesis 7:11–24
31   Genesis 7:11
32   Genesis 7:16
33   Genesis 8:4
34   Genesis 8:21–22
35   1 Samuel 16:7
36   Genesis 9:1–17
37   Genesis 22:12

The Bible in Cockney

Well, bits of it anyway...

Read how Jesus feeds five thousand geezers with just five loaves of Uncle Fred and two Lilian Gish. Or how Noah built a bloomin' massive nanny. Then there's always the story of David and that massive geezer Goliath, or the time when Simon's finger and thumb-in-law was Tom and Dick in Uncle Ned and Jesus healed her...

ISBN 1 84101 217 3   £5.99

More Bible in Cockney

Prophets, proverbs and pioneers

This book has a butcher's at some of the proverbs and psalms as well as the Ding Dong of Ding Dongs (Song of Songs). We'll find out about some of those great Old Testament prophets who got in a right old two-and-eight cos of the way the Israelites worshipped dodgy idols. To finish off, we have a complete translation of the Captain Hook of Acts into Cockney.

ISBN 1 84101 259 9   £6.99
Available from your local Christian bookshop or, in case of difficulty, direct from BRF using the order form on page 127.

★ ★ Also by Mike Coles ★ ★

So You Think You're a New Testament Writer

In an exclusive series of interviews, your host Mike Coles brings you five encounters with the men who shaped the New Testament. This is your chance to meet Matthew, Mark, Luke and John, as well as Paul. Is Paul's anti-women reputation deserved? Can we trust a reformed tax collector to tell the truth? What's the amazing new 'revelation' that John claims to have had on his island of exile? In *So You Think You're a New Testament Writer*, you'll find answers to these questions!

ISBN 1 84101 183 5   £6.99

God's Reality Show

Imagine Eve, Noah, Joseph, Moses, Joshua, Rahab, Deborah, Samson, Ruth, Saul and David lifted into the ultimate reality show, masterminded by the Lord God himself… Will the others gang up on Eve and blame her for bringing sin into the world? Will Saul and David simply end up killing each other? How will Samson conduct himself with the ladies? Find out what happens in *God's Reality Show*.

ISBN 1 84101 367 6   £6.99
Available from your local Christian bookshop or, in case of difficulty, direct from BRF using the order form on page 127.

★ ★ **Also by Mike Coles** ★ ★

Dear Bible, I Have a Problem

Many people love to read 'problem pages' in newspapers and magazines, where letters share a range of issues and the 'agony aunt' gives a suitable reply. *Dear Bible, I Have a Problem* takes this idea and imagines a range of people writing to… yes, the Bible, with their difficulties and problems, and what the Bible might say in reply!

Drawing on years of experience as a school counsellor and tutor, Mike Coles explores a wide selection of issues faced by many Christians—especially younger people—such as unanswered prayer, family hostility to faith, use and abuse of alcohol, and peer pressure, as well as more general problems such as loneliness, depression, stress, and worry about the future. Each situation is reviewed in the light of relevant biblical passages and, while there are seldom easy answers, the promise of God's help and comfort is always there.

ISBN 1 84101 368 4   £6.99
Available from your local Christian bookshop or, in case of difficulty, direct from BRF using the order form on page 127.

ORDER FORM

REF	TITLE	PRICE	QTY	TOTAL
217 3	The Bible in Cockney	£5.99		
259 9	More Bible in Cockney	£6.99		
183 5	So You Think You're a New Testament Writer	£6.99		
367 6	God's Reality Show	£6.99		
368 4	Dear Bible, I Have a Problem	£6.99		

POSTAGE AND PACKING CHARGES

order value	UK	Europe	Surface	Air Mail
£7.00 & under	£1.25	£3.00	£3.50	£5.50
£7.01–£30.00	£2.25	£5.50	£6.50	£10.00
Over £30.00	free	prices on request		

Postage and packing:

Donation:

Total enclosed:

Name _____ Account Number _____

Address _____

_____ Postcode _____

Telephone Number _____ Email _____

Payment by: ☐ Cheque ☐ Mastercard ☐ Visa ☐ Postal Order ☐ Switch

Card no. ☐☐☐☐ ☐☐☐☐ ☐☐☐☐ ☐☐☐☐

Expires ☐☐ ☐☐   Issue no. of Switch card ☐☐☐

Signature _____ Date _____

All orders must be accompanied by the appropriate payment.

Please send your completed order form to:
BRF, First Floor, Elsfield Hall, 15–17 Elsfield Way, Oxford OX2 8FG
Tel. 01865 319700 / Fax. 01865 319701 Email: enquiries@brf.org.uk

☐ Please send me further information about BRF publications.

Available from your local Christian bookshop.   BRF is a Registered Charity

brf

Resourcing your spiritual journey

through...

- Bible reading notes
- Books for Advent & Lent
- Books for Bible study and prayer
- Books to resource those working with under 11s in school, church and at home

- Quiet days and retreats
- Training for primary teachers and children's leaders
- Godly Play
- Barnabas Live

For more information, visit the **brf** website at **www.brf.org.uk**